Elementary Poetry

Textbook and Activity Book

by Sonja Glumich

Illustrations by Blanche Fisher Wright

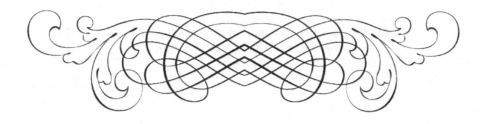

Poetry Study for Elementary School-Aged Children

Volume 1: The Enchanting Poetry of Mother Goose

Interweaves poetry, recitation, narration, drama, artwork, vocabulary, tracework, and copywork.

Under the Home Press Division
www.underthehome.org

Front Cover
Puddle Fun
Image by Holeysocksart
CC0 Creative Commons ({PD-US})
original source: *pixabay.com/en/boots-splash-rain-puddle-fun-774533/*

The Real Mother Goose, Original Copyright by Blanche Fisher Wright, 1916
Published by Rand McNally & Co.
Chicago

ISBN: 1948783029
ISBN-13: 978-1948783026

DEDICATION

For Chris, Everett, Cassidy, and Calista – my beloved family and curricula test squad.

TABLE OF CONTENTS

Lesson 1. Rain 1

Lesson 2. The Clock 4

Lesson 3. Fingers and Toes 7

Lesson 4. The Old Woman Under a Hill 10

Lesson 5. Oh, Dear! 13

Lesson 6. Pat-a-Cake 16

Lesson 7. Jack 19

Lesson 8. Baby Dolly 22

Lesson 9. Bees 25

Lesson 10. If Wishes Were Horses 28

Lesson 11. To Market 31

Lesson 12. Lucy Locket 34

Lesson 13. Two Birds 37

Lesson 14. The Flying Pig 40

Lesson 15. Hush-a-Bye 43

Lesson 16. The Three Wise Men of Gotham 46

Lesson 17. Pussy-Cat and Queen 49

Lesson 18. Christmas 52

Lesson 19. ABC 54

Lesson 20. Banbury Cross 57

Lesson 21. Wee Willie Winkie 60

Lesson 22. See-Saw 63

Lesson 23. Five Toes 66

Lesson 24. Three Blind Mice 69

Lesson 25. Diddle Diddle Dumpling 72

Lesson 26. The Black Hen 75

Lesson 27. A Candle 78

Lesson 28. Curly-Locks 81

Lesson 29. Humpty Dumpty 84

Lesson 30. Pins 87

Lesson 31. The Mouse and the Clock 90

Lesson 32. Jack Jelf 93

Lesson 33. Jack Sprat 96

Lesson 34. Hush-a-Bye 99

Lesson 35. Nancy Dawson 102

Lesson 36. The Alphabet 105

Lesson 37. Jack and Jill 108

Lesson 38. Dance to Your Daddy 111

Lesson 39. One Misty Moisty Morning 114

Lesson 40. The Old Woman From France 117

Lesson 41. My Kitten 120

Lesson 42. Pancake Day 123

Lesson 43. The Merchants of London 126

Lesson 44. Sleep Baby Sleep 129

Lesson 45. Baa Baa Black Sheep 132

Lesson 46. The Cat and the Fiddle 135

Lesson 47. Sing a Song of Sixpence 138

Lesson 48. Tommy Tittlemouse 142

Lesson 49. The Hobby-Horse 145

Lesson 50. Boy and the Sparrow 148

Lesson 51. Old Woman, Old Woman 151

Lesson 52. Two Pigeons 154

Lesson 53. The First of May 157
Lesson 54. Sulky Sue 160
Lesson 55. Bobby Snooks 163
Lesson 56. The Man in the Moon 166
Lesson 57. Poor Old Robinson Crusoe 169
Lesson 58. Cock-Crow 172
Lesson 59. Tommy Snooks 175
Lesson 60. The Blacksmith 178
Lesson 61. Cock-a-Doodle-Doo! 181
Lesson 62. Dapple-Gray 184
Lesson 63. Coffee and Tea 187
Lesson 64. The Little Girl with a Curl 190
Lesson 65. Candle-Saving 193
Lesson 66. Ladybird 196
Lesson 67. Caesar's Song 199
Lesson 68. As I Was Going Along 202
Lesson 69. Little Jack Horner 205
Lesson 70. Mary, Mary, Quite Contrary 208
Lesson 71. Mary's Canary 211
Lesson 72. The Little Bird 214

ANSWERS TO REVIEW QUESTIONS 217

REFERENCES AND ADDITIONAL READING 230

Goals of This Book Series

This book series aims to familiarize children with works of poetry from an early age, nurture the imagination, inspire an appreciation for beauty, encourage a mind for symbolism and nuance, foster the ability to narrate concepts and ideas, expand children's vocabularies, and develop children's hand-eye coordination and writing skills. Lessons are short and interactive by design to target elementary school-aged children.

Inspiration for This Book Series

Charlotte Mason, born in 1842, sought to provide teaching advice and strategies to instructors and homeschooling parents. She detailed her educational philosophies and methodologies in her multi-volume *Home Education Series*. She advocated for centering instruction around living works, such as the finest art, music, poetry, and prose. Mason recommended that from an early age, children engage in the regular study of poetry, including reciting poetry. In her *Home Education Series*, she writes, "…include a good deal of poetry, to accustom him to the delicate rendering of shades of meaning, and especially to make him aware that words are beautiful in themselves, that they are a source of pleasure, and are worthy of our honour; and that a beautiful word deserves to be beautifully said, with a certain roundness of tone and precision of utterance."

The Targeted Audience for This Book

This book targets elementary school-aged children in grades kindergarten through two.

Overview of This Book

This book provides 72 poetry lessons, or enough for two poetry lessons per week over a standard 36-week school year. This volume highlights the delightful poetry of Mother Goose. The selected poems in this book appeal to children and their adult instructors by featuring nature, animals, riddles, friendship, the seasons, holidays, trials, and triumphs.

How to Teach Using This Book

The table below outlines the recommended instructional approach to teach a 36-week course using this book.

Every Week – Introduce Two New Poems	
Section Title	**Section Instructions**
Featured Poem	Students recite poems line-by-line with instructor assistance.
Synopsis	Instructors read synopses of poems to students.
Recite Poem Information	Students practice reciting poem titles and the name of the poet.
Narrate the Poem	Students verbally summarize poems in their own words.
Study the Poem Picture	Students describe how poem pictures relate to poems.
Can You Find It?	Students find and point out items in poem pictures.
Act Out the Poem	Students act out aspects of poems.
Create Novel Artwork	Students create novel artwork based on poems.
Explore Rhyming	Instructors help students find and recite rhyming words in poems.
Vocabulary	• Students practice pronouncing featured vocabulary words. • Instructors read the definitions of vocabulary words to students.
Review Questions	Instructors ask students review questions. The end of the book contains answers to review questions.
Tracework and Copywork	Students trace and/or copy provided poem excerpts.
Color the Poem	Students color artwork related to poems.

The lessons in this book call for Legos, Play-Doh, blocks, and basic art supplies such as crayons, markers, paper, and scissors.

LESSON 1: "RAIN"

FEATURED POEM

Rain, rain, go away,

Come again another day;

Little Johnny wants to play.

SYNOPSIS

The narrator wishes the rain would go away so "little Johnny" can play outside.

ENRICHMENT ACTIVITIES

1. **Recite Poem Information**
   Practice reciting the title of the poem and the name of the poet.

2. **Narrate the Poem**
   Narrate the poem events or meaning aloud using your own words.

3. **Study the Poem Picture**
   Study the poem picture, and describe how it relates to the poem.

4. **Can You Find It?**
   Find the following in the poem picture: umbrella, little boy, jumping-jack toy, toy horse, duck, stream, birch tree trunk, rocks, rain drops, and jacket.

5. **Act Out the Poem**
   - If you have an umbrella, pretend it is raining and take shelter beneath it.
   - Pretend to splash through puddles.

6. **Create Novel Artwork Based on the Poem**
   - Create artwork associated with rain and umbrellas.
   - Use paints, crayons, pastels, glitter, Legos, blocks, or Play-Doh to create the artwork.

7. **Explore Rhyming**
   - Mother Goose poems often rhyme.
   - Words that rhyme have similar ending sounds.
   - The words in "Rain" that rhyme include *away*, *day*, and *play*.
   - Find and recite words that rhyme with the following: go, bye, and to.

VOCABULARY

Students Recite Words	Instructors Read Definitions to Students
poem	Lines of writing, generally rhymed.
rhyme	Sameness of sound of the end of words (e.g. away, day, and play).
narrator	The one telling a story.
again	Another time; once more.
want	To wish for.

REVIEW QUESTIONS

1. What is the title of the poem?

2. What happens in the poem?

3. What is the setting of the poem?

4. Who are the characters in the poem?

5. Does the poem teach us anything?

6. Describe the poem picture.

TRACEWORK AND/OR COPYWORK

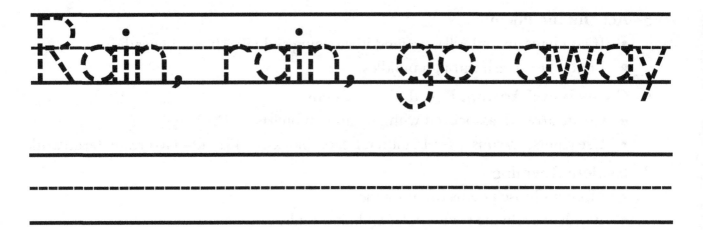

COLOR THE POEM

LESSON 2: "THE CLOCK"

FEATURED POEM

There's a neat little clock,--
In the schoolroom it stands,--
And it points to the time
With its two little hands.

And may we, like the clock,
Keep a face clean and bright,
With hands ever ready
To do what is right.

SYNOPSIS

The poem encourages children to be helpful and promotes habits of cleanliness.

ENRICHMENT ACTIVITIES

1. **Recite Poem Information**
   Practice reciting the title of the poem and the name of the poet.

2. **Narrate the Poem**
   Narrate the poem events or meaning aloud using your own words.

3. **Study the Poem Picture**
   Study the poem picture, and describe how it relates to the poem.

4. **Can You Find It?**
   Find the following in the poem picture: little girl, clock, two clock hands, two human hands, clock face, human face, dress, hat, and clock numbers.

5. **Act Out the Poem**
   • Take extra care washing your face and hands and brushing your teeth before you go to bed tonight.
   • Look for opportunities to help others.

6. **Create Novel Artwork Based on the Poem**
    - Create artwork that shows a child being helpful, washing their face, and/or brushing their teeth.
    - Use paints, crayons, pastels, Legos, blocks, or Play-Doh to create the artwork.

7. **Explore Rhyming**
   Find and recite the rhyming words in the poem.

VOCABULARY

Students Recite Words	Instructors Read Definitions to Students
neat	Clean, tidy; free from dirt.
clock	An instrument used to keep track of time.
schoolroom	A room in a school used to teach children.
stand	To support oneself on the feet in an erect position.
time	Moving into the future with the passing of events into the past.
hand	The part of a person's arm beyond the wrist including the palm and fingers.

REVIEW QUESTIONS

1. What is the title of the poem?

2. What happens in the poem?

3. What is the setting of the poem?

4. Who are the characters in the poem?

5. Does the poem teach us anything?

6. Describe the poem picture.

TRACEWORK AND/OR COPYWORK

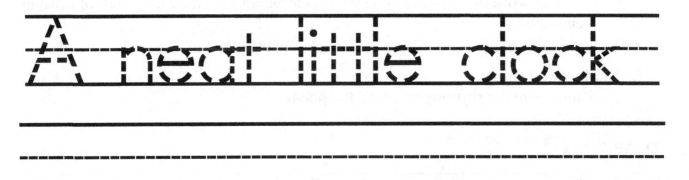

COLOR THE POEM

LESSON 3: "FINGERS AND TOES"

FEATURED POEM

Every lady in this land

Has twenty nails, upon each hand

Five, and twenty on hands and feet:

All this is true, without deceit.

SYNOPSIS

The poem is a riddle which demonstrates the importance of proper punctuation. Upon a first reading, the poem seems to make outlandish claims (every lady has 20 nails on each hand and every lady has 25 nails on hands and feet). Upon further examination, the poem only makes true statements (every lady has 20 nails, every lady has 5 nails upon each hand, and every lady has 20 nails upon hands and feet).

ENRICHMENT ACTIVITIES

1. **Recite Poem Information**
   Practice reciting the title of the poem and the name of the poet.

2. **Narrate the Poem**
   Narrate the poem events or meaning aloud using your own words.

3. **Study the Poem Picture**
   Study the poem picture, and describe how it relates to the poem.

4. **Can You Find It?**
   Find the following in the poem picture: lady, hands, feather, earring, and necklace.

5. **Act Out the Poem**
   - Count your fingernails and toenails. How many total nails do you have?
   - How many nails do you have on one hand?

6. **Create Novel Artwork Based on the Poem**
   - Trace an outline of your foot and your hand on paper.
   - Draw fingernails on the fingers and toenails on the toes.

7. **Explore Rhyming**
   Find and recite the rhyming words in the poem.

VOCABULARY

Students Recite Words	Instructors Read Definitions to Students
lady	A woman.
land	A country or region.
nail	The thin, hard plate at the ends of fingers and toes.
hand	The part of a person beyond the wrist including the palm and fingers.
feet	The part of a person beyond the ankle including the heel, instep, and toes.
true	Correct and accurate.
deceit	Lying or trickery.

REVIEW QUESTIONS

1. What is the title of the poem?

2. What happens in the poem?

3. Does the poem teach us anything?

4. What is the answer to the poem riddle?

TRACEWORK AND/OR COPYWORK

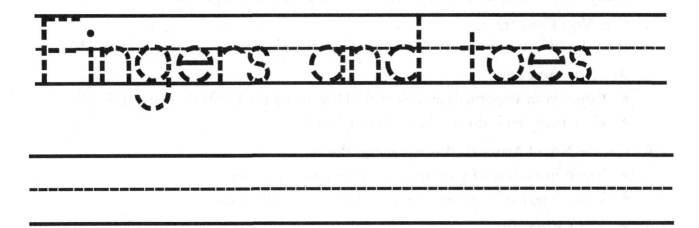

COLOR THE POEM

LESSON 4: "THE OLD WOMAN UNDER A HILL"

FEATURED POEM

There was an old woman

Lived under a hill;

And if she's not gone,

She lives there still.

SYNOPSIS

The poem is a logic joke, stating two things that together must obviously be true. If the woman is not gone from her house under the hill, she lives there still.

ENRICHMENT ACTIVITIES

1. **Recite Poem Information**
   Practice reciting the title of the poem and the name of the poet.

2. **Narrate the Poem**
   Narrate the poem events or meaning aloud using your own words.

3. **Study the Poem Picture**
   Study the poem picture, and describe how it relates to the poem.

4. **Can You Find It?**
   Find the following in the poem picture: old woman, hill, cave, rocks, houses, tree, gloves, sock, glasses, bench, bow, and spectacles.

5. **Act Out the Poem**
   - Make your own house under a hill.
   - Form a cave by clasping your hands over your head and circling your arms.
   - Practice reciting the poem in your cave.

6. **Create Novel Artwork Based on the Poem**
   - Create artwork of a house under a hill, including the doors, windows, and a chimney.
   - Use paints, crayons, pastels, Legos, blocks, or Play-Doh to create the artwork.

7. **Explore Rhyming**
   Find and recite the rhyming words in the poem.

VOCABULARY

Students Recite Words	Instructors Read Definitions to Students
old	A person having lived for most of the expected years.
hill	A high mound of earth smaller than a mountain.
gone	Away, having left.
still	Always or constantly.

REVIEW QUESTIONS

1. What is the title of the poem?

2. What happens in the poem?

3. Who are the characters in the poem?

4. Does the poem teach us anything?

5. Describe the poem picture.

TRACEWORK AND/OR COPYWORK

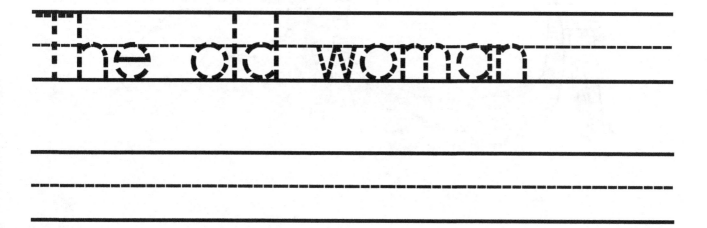

COLOR THE POEM

LESSON 5: "OH, DEAR!"

FEATURED POEM

Dear, dear! what can the matter be?

Two old women got up in an apple-tree;

One came down, and the other stayed till Saturday.

SYNOPSIS

Two old women climb an apple tree and come down at different times.

ENRICHMENT ACTIVITIES

1. **Recite Poem Information**
   Practice reciting the title of the poem and the name of the poet.

2. **Narrate the Poem**
   Narrate the poem events or meaning aloud using your own words.

3. **Study the Poem Picture**
   Study the poem picture, and describe how it relates to the poem.

4. **Can You Find It?**
   Find the following in the poem picture: old woman, apple tree, apples, clouds, sky, hill, dress, hat, and buckle.

5. **Act Out the Poem**
   - As you recite the poem, pretend to climb up an apple tree.
   - Raise your hands to indicate you've made it up in the tree.
   - As you continue to recite the poem, lower your hands to climb back down.

6. **Create Novel Artwork Based on the Poem**
   - One day this week, create artwork of an apple tree on a hill growing a huge apple.
   - Use paints, crayons, pastels, Legos, blocks, or Play-Doh to create the artwork.

7. **Explore Rhyming**
   Find and recite the rhyming words in the poem.

VOCABULARY

Students Recite Words	Instructors Read Definitions to Students
dear	A polite expression (oh dear) of surprise or worry.
woman	An adult female human.
apple	A common, round fruit produced by the tree Malus domestica.
tree	A large plant, typically with a single trunk and branches.
down	From a higher position to a lower one.
Saturday	The seventh day of the week; it follows Friday and precedes Sunday.

REVIEW QUESTIONS

1. What is the title of the poem?

2. What happens in the poem?

3. Who are the characters in the poem?

4. Describe the poem picture.

TRACEWORK AND/OR COPYWORK

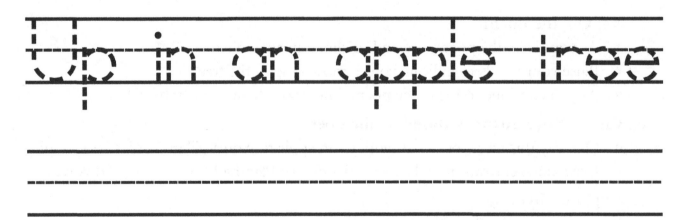

COLOR THE POEM

LESSON 6: "PAT-A-CAKE"

FEATURED POEM

Pat-a-cake, pat-a-cake,

Baker's man!

So I do, master,

As fast as I can.

Pat it, and prick it,

And mark it with T,

Put it in the oven

For Tommy and me.

SYNOPSIS

The narrator asks the baker's man to make a cake and gives him specific directions.

ENRICHMENT ACTIVITIES

1. **Recite Poem Information**
   Practice reciting the title of the poem and the name of the poet.

2. **Narrate the Poem**
   Narrate the poem events or meaning aloud using your own words.

3. **Study the Poem Picture**
   Study the poem picture, and describe how it relates to the poem.

4. **Can You Find It?**
   Find the following in the poem picture: baker's man, pie, bricks, fire, and pitcher.

5. **Act Out the Poem**
   - Perform the Pat-A-Cake hand play while reciting the rhyme.
   - Alternate clapping your hands and then slapping your legs.
   - For "pat it," pat your legs a few times.
   - For "mark it with T", punch your fist into the air.

6. **Create Novel Artwork Based on the Poem**
   - One day this week, create artwork of a delicious cake. Decorate your cake with frosting, sprinkles, and/or candles.
   - Use paints, crayons, glitter, pastels, Legos, blocks, or Play-Doh to create the artwork.

7. **Explore Rhyming**
Find and recite the rhyming words in the poem.

VOCABULARY

Students Recite Words	Instructors Read Definitions to Students
baker	A person who makes and sells bread, cakes, and similar items.
master	Someone who has control over something or someone.
pat	A light tap or slap, especially with the hands.
prick	An indentation or small mark made with a pointed object.
mark	To indent or scratch.
oven	A chamber used for baking or heating.

REVIEW QUESTIONS

1. What is the title of the poem?

2. What happens in the poem?

3. What is the setting of the poem?

4. Who are the characters in the poem?

5. Describe the poem picture.

TRACEWORK AND/OR COPYWORK

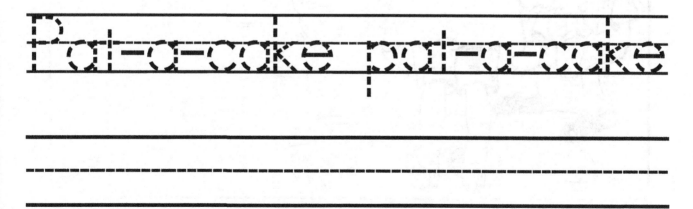

COLOR THE POEM

LESSON 7: "JACK"

FEATURED POEM

Jack be nimble, Jack be quick,

Jack jump over the candlestick.

SYNOPSIS

Nimble Jack jumps over a candlestick.

ENRICHMENT ACTIVITIES

1. **Recite Poem Information**
   Practice reciting the title of the poem and the name of the poet.

2. **Narrate the Poem**
   Narrate the poem events or meaning aloud using your own words.

3. **Study the Poem Picture**
   Study the poem picture, and describe how it relates to the poem.

4. **Can You Find It?**
   Find the following in the poem picture: Jack, candlestick, handle, candle, flame, smoke, hat, and tassel.

5. **Act Out the Poem**
   - Use a small object such as a pen or pencil as a candlestick.
   - Place your candlestick on a desk or table.
   - Using your pointer and middle fingers as "legs," pretend to run and jump over your "candlestick" while reciting the poem.

6. **Create Novel Artwork Based on the Poem**
   - One day this week, create artwork of a jumping boy.
   - Use paints, crayons, pastels, Legos, blocks, or Play-Doh to create the artwork.

7. **Explore Rhyming**
   Find and recite the rhyming words in the poem.

VOCABULARY

Students Recite Words	Instructors Read Definitions to Students
nimble	Quick and light in movement or action.
quick	Moving with speed.
candle	A light source consisting of a wick embedded in a solid, flammable substance.
candlestick	A holder with a socket or spike for a candle.

REVIEW QUESTIONS

1. What is the title of the poem?

2. What happens in the poem?

3. Who are the characters in the poem?

4. Does the poem teach us anything?

5. Describe the poem picture.

TRACEWORK AND/OR COPYWORK

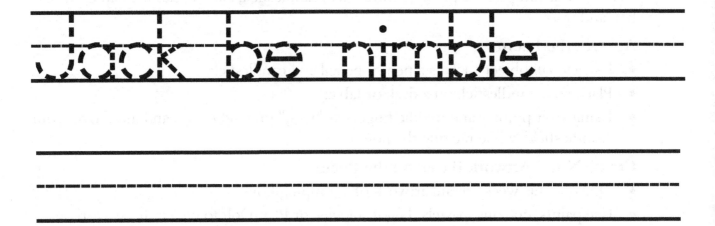

COLOR THE POEM

LESSON 8: "BABY DOLLY"

FEATURED POEM

Hush, baby, my dolly, I pray you don't cry,

And I'll give you some bread, and some milk by-and-by;

Or perhaps you like custard, or, maybe, a tart,

Then to either you're welcome, with all my heart.

SYNOPSIS

A little girl offers food to her fussy doll if the doll won't cry.

ENRICHMENT ACTIVITIES

1. **Recite Poem Information**
   Practice reciting the title of the poem and the name of the poet.

2. **Narrate the Poem**
   Narrate the poem events or meaning aloud using your own words.

3. **Study the Poem Picture**
   Study the poem picture, and describe how it relates to the poem.

4. **Can You Find It?**
   Find the following in the poem picture: little girl, dolly, rug, dresser, and mirror.

5. **Act Out the Poem**
   - Work with a partner with one person playing the little girl and the other the dolly.
   - The person playing the doll should pretend to cry while the person playing the little girl recites the poem and soothes the doll.

6. **Create Novel Artwork Based on the Poem**
   - One day this week, create artwork of a crying dolly. Don't forget to model the tears.
   - Use paints, crayons, pastels, Legos, blocks, or Play-Doh to create the artwork.

7. **Explore Rhyming**
   Find and recite the rhyming words in the poem.

VOCABULARY

Students Recite Words	Instructors Read Definitions to Students
hush	To become or make quiet.
pray	To petition or solicit help from a supernatural or higher being.
by-and-by	Immediately; at once.
custard	A type of sauce made from milk, eggs, sugar, and vanilla and thickened by heat.
tart	A type of small open pie.
heart	1. A muscular organ that pumps blood through the body. 2. Emotions, kindness, moral effort, or spirit in general.

REVIEW QUESTIONS

1. What is the title of the poem?

2. What happens in the poem?

3. Who are the characters in the poem?

4. Describe the poem picture.

TRACEWORK AND/OR COPYWORK

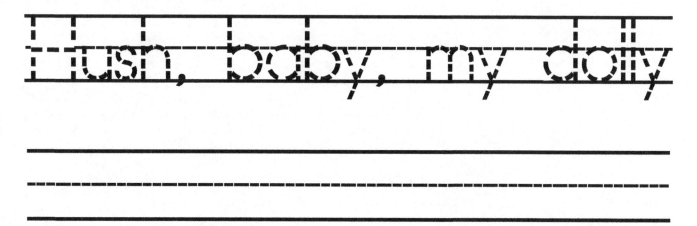

COLOR THE POEM

LESSON 9: "BEES"

FEATURED POEM

A swarm of bees in May

Is worth a load of hay;

A swarm of bees in June

Is worth a silver spoon;

A swarm of bees in July

Is not worth a fly.

SYNOPSIS

The poem expresses the times of year when bees are most needed for fertilizing crops.

ENRICHMENT ACTIVITIES

1. **Recite Poem Information**
   Practice reciting the title of the poem and the name of the poet.

2. **Narrate the Poem**
   Narrate the poem events or meaning aloud using your own words.

3. **Study the Poem Picture**
   Study the poem picture, and describe how it relates to the poem.

4. **Can You Find It?**
   Find the following in the poem picture: little child, tree, bees, swarm, hill, and cloud.

5. **Act Out the Poem**
   - Pretend your hand is a swarm of bees. Use your hand to show that bees are happy buzzing in their hive.
   - It is May. Use your hand to show that the swarm leaves their hive and fertilizes a few crops.
   - It is June and the bees' busy time. Use your hand to show that the swarm leaves their hive and fertilizes many, many crops.
   - It is July. Use your hand to show that the swarm stays in their hive and relaxes. There is little work to be done fertilizing now.

6. **Create Novel Artwork Based on the Poem**
   - One day this week, create artwork of a swarm of bees fertilizing some crops.
   - Use paints, crayons, pastels, Legos, blocks, or Play-Doh to create the artwork.

7. **Explore Rhyming**
   Find and recite the rhyming words in the poem.

VOCABULARY

Students Recite Words	Instructors Read Definitions to Students
bee	A flying insect, known collecting pollen and producing wax and honey.
swarm	A large number of insects, especially when in motion.
hay	Grass cut and dried for use as animal feed.
silver	A lustrous, white, metal.
fly	Any insect of the order Diptera; characterized by having two wings.
pollen	A fine yellow substance produced in plants such as flowers, transferred from plant to plant by insects and used for fertilization to grow new plants.
fertilize	To cause to produce offspring, such as new plants.

REVIEW QUESTIONS

1. What is the title of the poem?

2. What happens in the poem?

3. Does the poem teach us anything?

4. Describe the poem picture.

TRACEWORK AND/OR COPYWORK

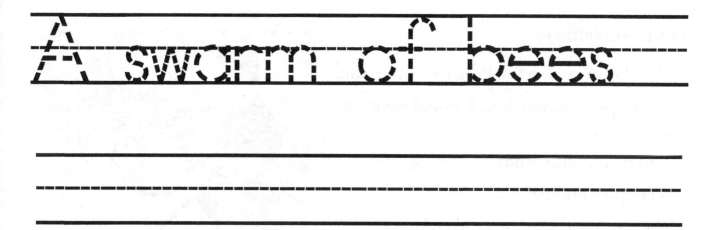

COLOR THE POEM

LESSON 10: "IF WISHES WERE HORSES"

FEATURED POEM

If wishes were horses, beggars would ride.

If turnips were watches, I would wear one by my side.

And if "ifs" and "ands"

Were pots and pans,

There'd be no work for tinkers!

SYNOPSIS

The poem states that if wishes could cause things to happen, even the poorest among us could have whatever they wanted. It also says if expensive items were inexpensive, everyone would have them. In addition, it states that if things that cost us nothing were valuable items, we would have an unlimited supply and they would never need to be repaired.

ENRICHMENT ACTIVITIES

1. **Recite Poem Information**
   Practice reciting the title of the poem and the name of the poet.

2. **Narrate the Poem**
   Narrate the poem events or meaning aloud using your own words.

3. **Study the Poem Picture**
   Study the poem picture, and describe how it relates to the poem.

4. **Can You Find It?**
   Find the following in the poem picture: horse, saddle, beggar, feather, path, and sign.

5. **Act Out the Poem**
   - Pretend wishes were horses.
   - Wish for a few things - imagine a horse appearing each time you wish.

6. **Create Novel Artwork Based on the Poem**
   - One day this week, create artwork of a herd of horses.
   - Use paints, crayons, pastels, Legos, blocks, or Play-Doh to create the artwork.

7. **Explore Rhyming**
   Find and recite the rhyming words in the poem.

VOCABULARY

Students Recite Words	Instructors Read Definitions to Students
wish	A desire, hope, or longing for something or for something to happen.
beggar	A person suffering from extreme poverty.
turnip	The white root of a yellow-flowered plant, grown as a vegetable and as feed for cattle.
watch	A portable or wearable timepiece.
tinker	A person who makes and mends household utensils made of tin.

REVIEW QUESTIONS

1. What is the title of the poem?

2. What happens in the poem?

3. Who are the characters in the poem?

4. Does the poem teach us anything?

5. Describe the poem picture.

TRACEWORK AND/OR COPYWORK

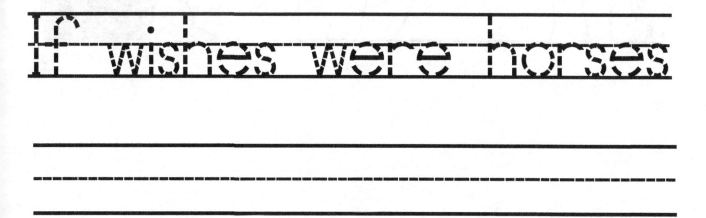

COLOR THE POEM

LESSON 11: "TO MARKET"

FEATURED POEM

To market, to market, to buy a fat pig.

Home again, home again, jiggety jig.

To market, to market, to buy a fat hog,

Home again, home again, jiggety jog.

To market, to market, to buy a plum bun,

Home again, home again, market is done.

SYNOPSIS

The narrator visits a market and makes purchases.

ENRICHMENT ACTIVITIES

1. **Recite Poem Information**
   Practice reciting the title of the poem and the name of the poet.

2. **Narrate the Poem**
   Narrate the poem events or meaning aloud using your own words.

3. **Study the Poem Picture**
   Study the poem picture, and describe how it relates to the poem.

4. **Can You Find It?**
   Find the following in the poem picture: boy, girl, bonnet, bow, ribbon, leash, pig, and basket.

5. **Act Out the Poem**
   - Work with a partner.
   - Draw, color, and cut out some money, a bun, and a pig.
   - Have one partner act as the buyer and the other as the seller.
   - Exchange the paper money, pig, and bun as you recite the poem.

6. **Create Novel Artwork Based on the Poem**
   - One day this week, create artwork of a busy marketplace. Show the many different things being bought and sold.
   - Use paints, crayons, pastels, Legos, blocks, or Play-Doh to create the artwork.

7. **Explore Rhyming**
Find and recite the rhyming words in the poem.

VOCABULARY

Students Recite Words	Instructors Read Definitions to Students
market	Site where traders set up stalls and buyers browse the merchandise.
jig	A light, brisk musical movement.
hog	An adult pig.
plum	A desirable thing.
bun	A small bread roll, often sweetened or spiced.

REVIEW QUESTIONS

1. What is the title of the poem?

2. What happens in the poem?

3. What is the setting of the poem?

4. Who are the characters in the poem?

5. Describe the poem picture.

TRACEWORK AND/OR COPYWORK

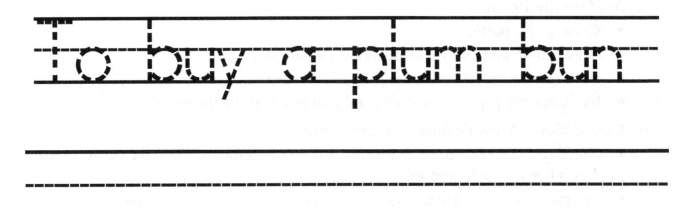

COLOR THE POEM

LESSON 12: "LUCY LOCKET"

FEATURED POEM

Lucy Locket lost her pocket,

Kitty Fisher found it;

Nothing in it, nothing in it,

But the binding round it.

SYNOPSIS

Lucy Locket loses her pocket. Kitty Fisher finds it and returns it to her, but it is empty.

ENRICHMENT ACTIVITIES

1. **Recite Poem Information**
   Practice reciting the title of the poem and the name of the poet.

2. **Narrate the Poem**
   Narrate the poem events or meaning aloud using your own words.

3. **Study the Poem Picture**
   Study the poem picture, and describe how it relates to the poem.

4. **Can You Find It?**
   Find the following in the poem picture: Lucy Locket, Kitty Fisher, the empty pocket, hand muff, house, trees, bush, handkerchief, and snow.

5. **Act Out the Poem**
   - With a partner, get a small object to play "hot and cold."
   - One person acts as the seeker and leaves the room.
   - The other acts as the hider and hides the object.
   - The hider calls the seeker back to the room to find the object.
   - The hider calls out "hot" or "cold" depending on whether the seeker is moving closer (hot) or farther (cold) from the hidden object.

6. **Create Novel Artwork Based on the Poem**
   - One day this week, create artwork of a locket.
   - Use paints, crayons, pastels, Legos, blocks, or Play-Doh to create the artwork.

7. **Explore Rhyming**
   Find and recite the rhyming words in the poem.

VOCABULARY

Students Recite Words	Instructors Read Definitions to Students
locket	A pendant that opens to reveal a space used for storing a photograph.
pocket	A bag used for carrying small items.
binding	An item (usually thread, tape, or string) used to hold two or more things together.

REVIEW QUESTIONS

1. What is the title of the poem?

2. What happens in the poem?

3. Who are the characters in the poem?

4. Does the poem teach us anything?

5. Describe the poem picture.

TRACEWORK AND/OR COPYWORK

COLOR THE POEM

LESSON 13: "TWO BIRDS"

FEATURED POEM

There were two birds sat on a stone,

Fa, la, la, la, lal, de;

One flew away, and then there was one,

Fa, la, la, la, lal, de;

The other bird flew after,

And then there was none,

Fa, la, la, la, lal, de;

And so the stone

Was left alone,

Fa, la, la, la, lal, de.

SYNOPSIS

Two birds sit on a stone. One by one they fly away, leaving the stone alone.

ENRICHMENT ACTIVITIES

1. **Recite Poem Information**
   Practice reciting the title of the poem and the name of the poet.

2. **Narrate the Poem**
   Narrate the poem events or meaning aloud using your own words.

3. **Study the Poem Picture**
   Study the poem picture, and describe how it relates to the poem.

4. **Can You Find It?**
   Find the following in the poem picture: sitting bird, flying bird, stones, clouds, house, and hill.

5. **Act Out the Poem**
   - Act out that two birds (your two hands) sit on a stone (pencil).
   - As you recite the poem, have your hands fly away from the pencil in time with the poem.

6. **Create Novel Artwork Based on the Poem**
    - One day this week, create artwork of a bird soaring away from a stone.
    - Use paints, crayons, pastels, Legos, blocks, or Play-Doh to create the artwork.

7. **Explore Rhyming**
    Find and recite the rhyming words in the poem.

VOCABULARY

Students Recite Words	Instructors Read Definitions to Students
stone	A hard earthen substance that can form large rocks; a rock.
flew	Traveled through the air.
alone	By oneself, solitary.

REVIEW QUESTIONS

1. What is the title of the poem?

2. What happens in the poem?

3. What is the setting of the poem?

4. Does the poem teach us anything?

5. Describe the poem picture.

TRACEWORK AND/OR COPYWORK

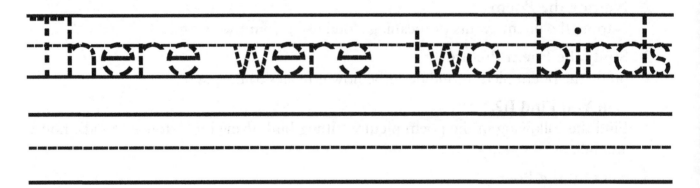

There were two birds

COLOR THE POEM

LESSON 14: "THE FLYING PIG"

FEATURED POEM

Dickory, dickory, dare,

The pig flew up in the air;

The man in brown soon brought him down,

Dickory, dickory, dare.

SYNOPSIS

A pig flies into the air, but a man in brown brings him back down.

ENRICHMENT ACTIVITIES

1. **Recite Poem Information**
   Practice reciting the title of the poem and the name of the poet.

2. **Narrate the Poem**
   Narrate the poem events or meaning aloud using your own words.

3. **Study the Poem Picture**
   Study the poem picture, and describe how it relates to the poem.

4. **Can You Find It?**
   Find the following in the poem picture: man, children, kite, kite tail, pig, and cloud.

5. **Act Out the Poem**
   - As you recite the poem, use your hands to act out the roles of the flying pig and the man in brown.
   - Have of your hands (pig) pretend to fly through the air, until the other hand (man) brings it back down.

6. **Create Novel Artwork Based on the Poem**
   - One day this week, create artwork of a flying pig with wings.
   - Use paints, crayons, pastels, Legos, blocks, or Play-Doh to create the artwork.

7. **Explore Rhyming**
   Find and recite the rhyming words in the poem.

VOCABULARY

Students Recite Words	Instructors Read Definitions to Students
dare	To have enough courage (to do something).
air	The gaseous substance encompassing the earth.
kite	A lightweight toy carried on the wind and controlled from the ground by a string.
brown	A color like that of chocolate or coffee.

REVIEW QUESTIONS

1. What is the title of the poem?

2. What happens in the poem?

3. Who are the characters in the poem?

4. Does the poem teach us anything?

5. Describe the poem picture.

TRACEWORK AND/OR COPYWORK

COLOR THE POEM

LESSON 15: "HUSH-A-BYE"

FEATURED POEM

Hush-a-bye, baby, on the tree top!

When the wind blows the cradle will rock;

When the bough breaks the cradle will fall;

Down will come baby, bough, cradle and all.

SYNOPSIS

A baby rocks in a cradle and falls from a tree.

ENRICHMENT ACTIVITIES

1. **Recite Poem Information**
   Practice reciting the title of the poem and the name of the poet.

2. **Narrate the Poem**
   Narrate the poem events or meaning aloud using your own words.

3. **Study the Poem Picture**
   Study the poem picture, and describe how it relates to the poem.

4. **Can You Find It?**
   Find the following in the poem picture: tree, bough, cradle, baby, pillow, and ropes.

5. **Act Out the Poem**
   - As you recite the poem, rock a pencil or small unbreakable object in your hand.
   - When the baby in the poem falls, gently drop the object onto your desk or table.

6. **Create Novel Artwork Based on the Poem**
   - One day this week, create artwork of a baby up in a tree.
   - Use paints, crayons, pastels, Legos, blocks, or Play-Doh to create the artwork.

7. **Explore Rhyming**
   Find and recite the rhyming words in the poem.

VOCABULARY

Students Recite Words	Instructors Read Definitions to Students
wind	The movement of air.
cradle	A bed or cot for a baby that can sway back and forth.
rock	To move gently back and forth.
bough	A firm branch of a tree.
fall	The act of moving to a lower position due to gravity.

REVIEW QUESTIONS

1. What is the title of the poem?

2. What happens in the poem?

3. What is the setting of the poem?

4. Who are the characters in the poem?

5. Describe the poem picture.

TRACEWORK AND/OR COPYWORK

COLOR THE POEM

LESSON 16: "THE THREE WISE MEN OF GOTHAM"

FEATURED POEM

Three wise men of Gotham

Went to sea in a bowl;

If the bowl had been stronger

My song had been longer.

SYNOPSIS

Three men set out to sea in a bowl. Unsurprisingly, they never return.

ENRICHMENT ACTIVITIES

1. **Recite Poem Information**
   Practice reciting the title of the poem and the name of the poet.

2. **Narrate the Poem**
   Narrate the poem events or meaning aloud using your own words.

3. **Study the Poem Picture**
   Study the poem picture, and describe how it relates to the poem.

4. **Can You Find It?**
   Find the following in the poem picture: three men, spyglass, bowl, ocean, waves, birds, and beard.

5. **Act Out the Poem**
   - Place three small items, such as crayons, in your cupped hands to represent the men.
   - Rock your hands back and forth to simulate the ocean waves, and recite the poem.

6. **Create Novel Artwork Based on the Poem**
   - One day this week, create artwork of the large waves of the sea.
   - Use paints, crayons, pastels, Legos, blocks, or Play-Doh to create the artwork.

7. **Explore Rhyming**
   Find and recite the rhyming words in the poem.

VOCABULARY

Students Recite Words	Instructors Read Definitions to Students
wise	Showing good judgement or the benefit of experience.
Gotham	A village in Nottinghamshire, England, associated in folklore with insanity.
bowl	A curved container used to hold, mix, or present food, such as salad, fruit, or soup.
stronger	More capable of withstanding great physical force.
longer	A greater duration.

REVIEW QUESTIONS

1. What is the title of the poem?

2. What happens in the poem?

3. What is the setting of the poem?

4. Who are the characters in the poem?

5. Were the wise men of Gotham in the poem actually wise?

6. Does the poem teach us anything?

7. Describe the poem picture.

TRACEWORK AND/OR COPYWORK

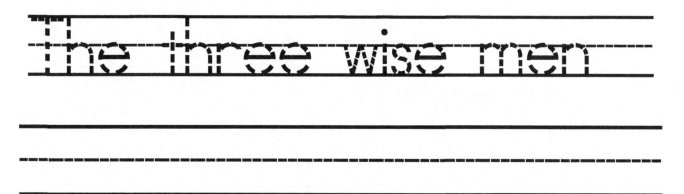

COLOR THE POEM

LESSON 17: "PUSSY-CAT AND QUEEN"

FEATURED POEM

"Pussy-cat, pussy-cat,

Where have you been?"

"I've been to London

To look at the Queen."

"Pussy-cat, pussy-cat,

What did you there?"

"I frightened a little mouse

Under the chair."

SYNOPSIS

A cat tells the narrator of his travel to London to see the Queen. While there, the cat scares a mouse under a chair.

ENRICHMENT ACTIVITIES

1. **Recite Poem Information**
   Practice reciting the title of the poem and the name of the poet.

2. **Narrate the Poem**
   Narrate the poem events or meaning aloud using your own words.

3. **Study the Poem Picture**
   Study the poem picture, and describe how it relates to the poem.

4. **Can You Find It?**
   Find the following in the poem picture: girl, basket, umbrella, bonnet, cat, fence, farm, and path.

5. **Act Out the Poem**
   - Pretend your hands are the cat and the mouse from the poem.
   - As you read the poem, act out the cat scaring the mouse under the chair. (One hand might hide under your desk, table, or chair.)

6. **Create Novel Artwork Based on the Poem**
   - One day this week, create artwork of the mouse hiding under a chair.
   - Use paints, crayons, pastels, Legos, blocks, or Play-Doh to create the artwork.

7. **Explore Rhyming**
   Find and recite the rhyming words in the poem.

VOCABULARY

Students Recite Words	Instructors Read Definitions to Students
London	The capital city of the United Kingdom and of England.
Queen	A female ruler of a country.
mouse	A small rodent.
chair	An item of furniture used to sit on.

REVIEW QUESTIONS

1. What is the title of the poem?

2. What happens in the poem?

3. What is the setting of the poem?

4. Who are the characters in the poem?

5. Describe the poem picture.

TRACEWORK AND/OR COPYWORK

COLOR THE POEM

SONJA GLUMICH

LESSON 18: "CHRISTMAS"

FEATURED POEM

Christmas comes but once a year,

And when it comes it brings good cheer.

SYNOPSIS

The poem points out that Christmas is rare but lots of fun.

ENRICHMENT ACTIVITIES

1. **Recite Poem Information**
   Practice reciting the title of the poem and the name of the poet.

2. **Narrate the Poem**
   Narrate the poem events or meaning aloud using your own words.

3. **Study the Poem Picture**
   Study the poem picture, and describe how it relates to the poem.

4. **Can You Find It?**
   Find the following in the poem picture: Christmas tree, star, candles, ornaments, trunk, garland, and tree stand.

5. **Create Novel Artwork Based on the Poem**
   - One day this week, create artwork of a Christmas tree decorated with ornaments.
   - Use paints, crayons, pastels, Legos, blocks, or Play-Doh to create the artwork.

6. **Explore Rhyming**
   Find and recite the rhyming words in the poem.

VOCABULARY

Students Recite Words	Instructors Read Definitions to Students
year	1. A period between dates that mark a year, such as from January 1 to December 31. 2. The time it takes the Earth to complete one revolution of the Sun.
cheer	A cheerful attitude; gaiety; mirth.

REVIEW QUESTIONS

1. What is the title of the poem?
2. What happens in the poem?
3. Describe the poem picture.

TRACEWORK AND/OR COPYWORK

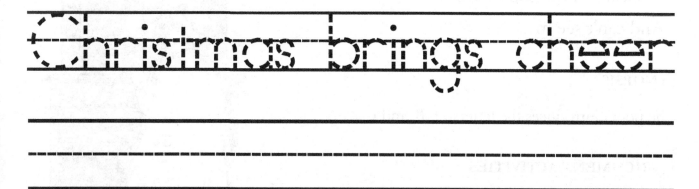

COLOR THE POEM

LESSON 19: "ABC"

FEATURED POEM

Great A, little a,

Bouncing B!

The cat's in the cupboard,

And can't see me.

SYNOPSIS

The poem introduces the letters *A*, *B*, and *C*.

ENRICHMENT ACTIVITIES

1. **Recite Poem Information**
   Practice reciting the title of the poem and the name of the poet.

2. **Narrate the Poem**
   Narrate the poem events or meaning aloud using your own words.

3. **Study the Poem Picture**
   Study the poem picture, and describe how it relates to the poem.

4. **Can You Find It?**
   Find the following letters in the poem: Great *A*, little *a*, bouncing *B*, and *c*. Find letters in the poem picture as well.

5. **Act Out the Poem**
   - As you recite the poem, clasp your hands over your head to form a capital A.
   - Bounce up and down in your seat like a bouncing B.
   - Curve your hand into a C shape when you say *cat*, *cupboard*, and *can't* during the poem.

6. **Create Novel Artwork Based on the Poem**
   - One day this week, create three-dimensional models of the letters A, B, and C.
   - Use Legos, blocks, or Play-Doh to create the letters.

7. **Explore Rhyming**
   Find and recite the rhyming words (including letters) in the poem.

VOCABULARY

Students Recite Words	Instructors Read Definitions to Students
great	Very big in size.
little	Small in size.
bouncing	Moving quickly up and down.
cupboard	A cabinet, closet, or other piece of furniture with shelves intended for storing cookware, dishware, or food.

REVIEW QUESTIONS

1. What is the title of the poem?

2. Does the poem teach us anything?

3. Who are the characters in the poem?

4. Describe the poem picture.

TRACEWORK AND/OR COPYWORK

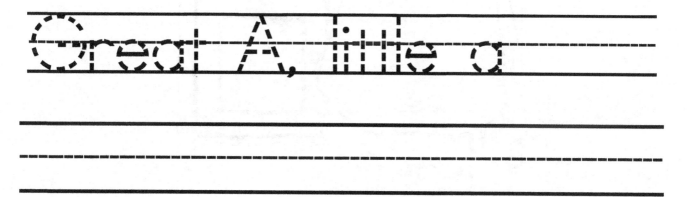

COLOR THE POEM

LESSON 20: "BANBURY CROSS"

FEATURED POEM

Ride a cock-horse to Banbury Cross,

To see an old lady upon a white horse.

Rings on her fingers, and bells on her toes,

She shall have music wherever she goes.

SYNOPSIS

A lady rides a horse to Banbury Cross with bells on her toes, making music wherever she goes.

ENRICHMENT ACTIVITIES

1. **Recite Poem Information**
   Practice reciting the title of the poem and the name of the poet.

2. **Narrate the Poem**
   Narrate the poem events or meaning aloud using your own words.

3. **Study the Poem Picture**
   Study the poem picture, and describe how it relates to the poem.

4. **Can You Find It?**
   Find the following in the poem picture: lady, toes, bells, horse, rings, feather, gloves, basket, and baby.

5. **Act Out the Poem**
   • As you recite the poem, pretend to ride a horse and gallop in your chair.
   • Make a noise like the tinkle of a bell at the end of the poem.

6. **Create Novel Artwork Based on the Poem**
   • One day this week, create rings for the lady's fingers and bells for her toes.
   • Use paints, crayons, pastels, Legos, blocks, or Play-Doh to create the artwork.

7. **Explore Rhyming**
   Find and recite the rhyming words in the poem.

VOCABULARY

Students Recite Words	Instructors Read Definitions to Students
Banbury	A market town and civil parish in England.
cross	A place where roads intersect and lead off in four directions; a crossroad.
cock-horse	Something a child can ride as though on horseback; a toy hobby-horse.
rings	Round pieces of precious metal worn around the fingers.
bells	Instruments often made of metal and shaped like an inverted cup with a flared rim, which rings or gongs when struck.
music	Any pleasing or interesting sounds.

REVIEW QUESTIONS

1. What is the title of the poem?

2. What happens in the poem?

3. What is the setting of the poem?

4. Who are the characters in the poem?

5. Describe the poem picture.

TRACEWORK AND/OR COPYWORK

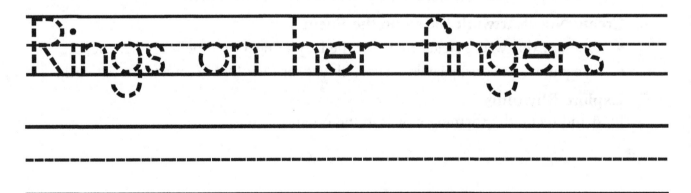

COLOR THE POEM

LESSON 21: "WEE WILLIE WINKIE"

FEATURED POEM

Wee Willie Winkie runs through the town,

Upstairs and downstairs, in his nightgown;

Rapping at the window, crying through the lock,

"Are the children in their beds? Now it's eight o'clock."

SYNOPSIS

Wee Willie Winkie runs through the town, making sure the children are in bed. Some interpretations of the poem view Willie Winkie as a personification of sleep visiting all the children.

ENRICHMENT ACTIVITIES

1. **Recite Poem Information**
   Practice reciting the title of the poem and the name of the poet.

2. **Narrate the Poem**
   Narrate the poem events or meaning aloud using your own words.

3. **Study the Poem Picture**
   Study the poem picture, and describe how it relates to the poem.

4. **Can You Find It?**
   Find the following in the poem picture: Willie, nightgown, nightcap, bench, stairs, window, and shutter.

5. **Act Out the Poem**
   - *Wee Willie Winkie runs through the town,* (Run two fingers across your table.)
   - *Upstairs and downstairs, in his nightgown;* (Lift your hands for upstairs, lower them for downstairs.)
   - *Rapping at the window, crying through the lock,* (Knock on your table, and then wring your fists below your eyes like you are crying.)
   - *Are the children in their beds? Now it's eight o'clock.* (Cup your hands like a bullhorn to your mouth.)

6. **Create Novel Artwork Based on the Poem**
   - One day this week, draw or model what *sleep* might look like in the form of a person.
   - Use paints, crayons, pastels, Legos, blocks, or Play-Doh to create the artwork.

7. **Explore Rhyming**
   Find and recite the rhyming words in the poem.

VOCABULARY

Students Recite Words	Instructors Read Definitions to Students
wee	Small, little.
upstairs	Located on a higher floor or level of a building.
downstairs	Located on a lower floor or level of a building.
rapping	Sharp blows with something hard.
lock	Something used for fastening, which can only be opened with a key or combination.

REVIEW QUESTIONS

1. What is the title of the poem?

2. What happens in the poem?

3. What is the setting of the poem?

4. Who are the characters in the poem?

5. Does the poem teach us anything?

6. Describe the poem picture.

TRACEWORK AND/OR COPYWORK

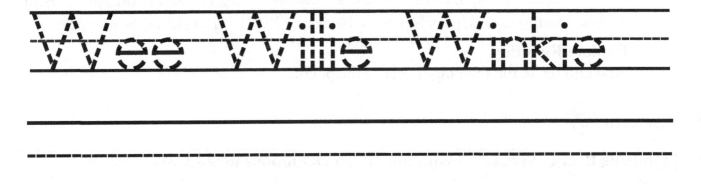

COLOR THE POEM

LESSON 22: "SEE-SAW"

FEATURED POEM

See-saw, Margery Daw,

Sold her bed and lay upon straw.

SYNOPSIS

This poem contains a rhyme for children to recite as they move up and down on a seesaw.

ENRICHMENT ACTIVITIES

1. **Recite Poem Information**
   Practice reciting the title of the poem and the name of the poet.

2. **Narrate the Poem**
   Narrate the poem events or meaning aloud using your own words.

3. **Study the Poem Picture**
   Study the poem picture, and describe how it relates to the poem.

4. **Can You Find It?**
   Find the following in the poem picture: children, beehive, bees, rock, boy's hat, bow, tree, wooden board, shoe buckle, and seesaw.

5. **Act Out the Poem**
   As you recite the poem pretend to ride a seesaw by nodding your head up and down.

6. **Create Novel Artwork Based on the Poem**
   - One day this week, create a three-dimensional sculpture of a seesaw.
   - Use Legos, blocks, or Play-Doh to create the seesaw.

7. **Explore Rhyming**
   Find and recite the rhyming words in the poem.

VOCABULARY

Students Recite Words	Instructors Read Definitions to Students
see-saw (seesaw)	A structure composed of a plank, balanced in the middle, used as a game in which one person goes up as the other goes down; a teeter-totter.
sold	Transferred goods in exchange for money.
straw	Dried stalks of a cereal plant.

REVIEW QUESTIONS

1. What is the title of the poem?

2. What happens in the poem?

3. Who are the characters in the poem?

4. Describe the poem picture.

TRACEWORK AND/OR COPYWORK

COLOR THE POEM

LESSON 23: "FIVE TOES"

FEATURED POEM

This little pig went to market;

This little pig stayed at home;

This little pig had roast beef;

This little pig had none;

This little pig said, "Wee, wee!

I can't find my way home."

SYNOPSIS

The poem refers to each of the five toes on a little foot.

ENRICHMENT ACTIVITIES

1. **Recite Poem Information**
   Practice reciting the title of the poem and the name of the poet.

2. **Narrate the Poem**
   Narrate the poem events or meaning aloud using your own words.

3. **Study the Poem Picture**
   Study the poem picture, and describe how it relates to the poem.

4. **Can You Find It?**
   Find the following in the poem picture: baby, toes, cap, bow, chair, and drapes.

5. **Act Out the Poem**
   - As you recite the poem, touch your fingers or your toes for the little pigs.
   - Wiggle all of your fingers or toes as the last piggy says, "Wee, wee! I can't find my way home."

6. **Create Novel Artwork Based on the Poem**
   - One day this week, create artwork of a piggy visiting a market.
   - Use paints, crayons, pastels, Legos, blocks, or Play-Doh to create the artwork.

7. **Explore Rhyming**
   Find and recite the rhyming words in the poem.

VOCABULARY

Students Recite Words	Instructors Read Definitions to Students
market	Site where traders set up stalls and buyers browse the merchandise.
roast beef	Beef cooked by roasting.
none	Not any.

REVIEW QUESTIONS

1. What is the title of the poem?

2. What happens in the poem?

3. Who are the characters in the poem?

4. Describe the poem picture.

TRACEWORK AND/OR COPYWORK

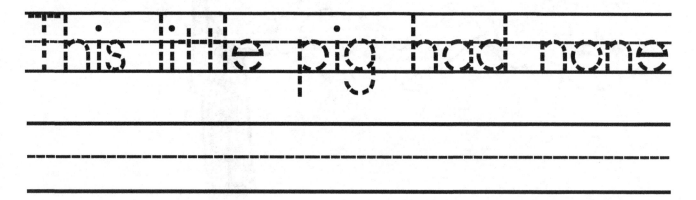

COLOR THE POEM

LESSON 24: "THREE BLIND MICE"

FEATURED POEM

Three blind mice! See how they run!

They all ran after the farmer's wife,

Who cut off their tails with a carving knife.

Did you ever see such a thing in your life

As three blind mice?

SYNOPSIS

Three blind mice chase a farmer's wife, and she retaliates.

ENRICHMENT ACTIVITIES

1. **Recite Poem Information**
   Practice reciting the title of the poem and the name of the poet.

2. **Narrate the Poem**
   Narrate the poem events or meaning aloud using your own words.

3. **Study the Poem Picture**
   Study the poem picture, and describe how it relates to the poem.

4. **Can You Find It?**
   Find the following in the poem picture: farmer's wife, three mice, something overturned, cupboard, plates, cabinet, and apron.

5. **Act Out the Poem**
   - Use your hands to play the roles of the mice and the farmer's wife.
   - As you recite the poem, act out the three mice chasing the farmer's wife around the table.

6. **Create Novel Artwork Based on the Poem**
   - One day this week, create artwork of the three blind mice.
   - Use paints, crayons, pastels, Legos, blocks, or Play-Doh to create the artwork.

7. **Explore Rhyming**
   Find and recite the rhyming words in the poem.

VOCABULARY

Students Recite Words	Instructors Read Definitions to Students
blind	Unable to see.
mice	Small rodents with long tails.
farmer	A person who works the land and/or who keeps livestock, especially on a farm.
wife	A married woman.

REVIEW QUESTIONS

1. What is the title of the poem?

2. What happens in the poem?

3. Who are the characters in the poem?

4. Describe the poem picture.

TRACEWORK AND/OR COPYWORK

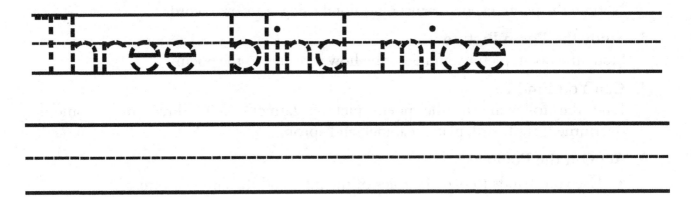

COLOR THE POEM

LESSON 25: "DIDDLE DIDDLE DUMPLING"

FEATURED POEM

Diddle diddle dumpling, my son John

Went to bed with his breeches on,

One stocking off, and one stocking on;

Diddle diddle dumpling, my son John.

SYNOPSIS

John falls asleep wearing his breeches and only one sock.

ENRICHMENT ACTIVITIES

1. **Recite Poem Information**
   Practice reciting the title of the poem and the name of the poet.

2. **Narrate the Poem**
   Narrate the poem events or meaning aloud using your own words.

3. **Study the Poem Picture**
   Study the poem picture, and describe how it relates to the poem.

4. **Can You Find It?**
   Find the following in the poem picture: John, one sock on, one sock off, breeches, bed, candle, window, bed skirt, and pillow.

5. **Act Out the Poem**
   As you recite the poem, while remaining in your chair, pretend to remove one sock and fall asleep.

6. **Create Novel Artwork Based on the Poem**
   - One day this week, create artwork of a single sock with a wacky pattern.
   - Use paints, crayons, pastels, Legos, blocks, or Play-Doh to create the artwork.

7. **Explore Rhyming**
   Find and recite the rhyming words in the poem.

VOCABULARY

Students Recite Words	Instructors Read Definitions to Students
son	One's male offspring.
breeches	Trousers; pants.
stocking	A man's sock.

REVIEW QUESTIONS

1. What is the title of the poem?

2. What happens in the poem?

3. What is the setting of the poem?

4. Who are the characters in the poem?

5. Describe the poem picture.

TRACEWORK AND/OR COPYWORK

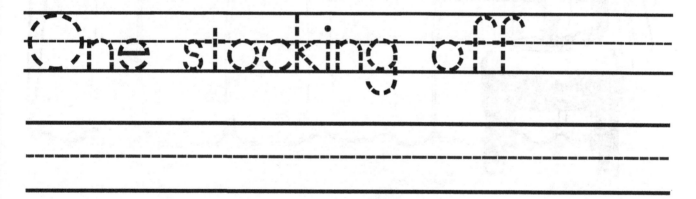

COLOR THE POEM

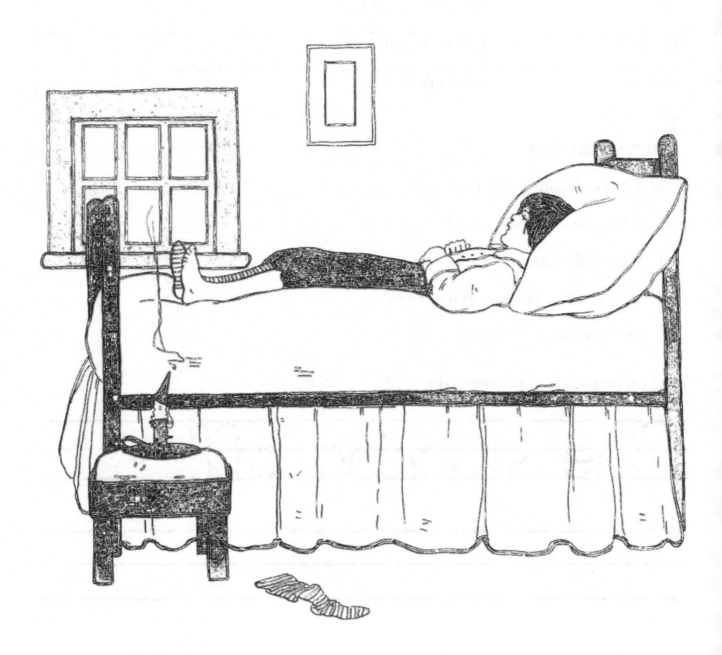

LESSON 26: "THE BLACK HEN"

FEATURED POEM

Hickety, pickety, my black hen,

She lays eggs for gentlemen;

Gentlemen come every day

To see what my black hen doth lay.

SYNOPSIS

A black hen lays eggs for gentlemen.

ENRICHMENT ACTIVITIES

1. **Recite Poem Information**
   Practice reciting the title of the poem and the name of the poet.

2. **Narrate the Poem**
   Narrate the poem events or meaning aloud using your own words.

3. **Study the Poem Picture**
   Study the poem picture, and describe how it relates to the poem.

4. **Can You Find It?**
   Find the following in the poem picture: black hen, nest, gentlemen, basket, umbrella, and hats.

5. **Act Out the Poem**
   - Pretend your hand is the black hen.
   - Cluck, scratch, peck, and flap your finger wings as you strut about your table or desk.
   - Pretend to lay some eggs for the gentlemen.

6. **Create Novel Artwork Based on the Poem**
   - One day this week, create artwork of a nest of eggs
   - Use paints, crayons, pastels, Legos, blocks, or Play-Doh to create the artwork.

7. **Explore Rhyming**
   Find and recite the rhyming words in the poem.

VOCABULARY

Students Recite Words	Instructors Read Definitions to Students
hen	A female chicken.
gentlemen	A man of gentle but not noble birth, particularly a man of means (originally ownership of property) who does not work for a living.
doth	Archaic term for *does*.
lay	To produce and deposit an egg.

REVIEW QUESTIONS

1. What is the title of the poem?

2. What happens in the poem?

3. What is the setting of the poem?

4. Who are the characters in the poem?

5. Describe the poem picture.

TRACEWORK AND/OR COPYWORK

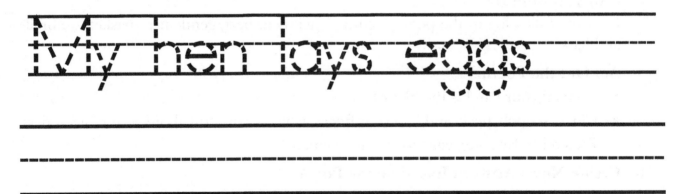

COLOR THE POEM

LESSON 27: "A CANDLE"

FEATURED POEM

Little Nanny Etticoat

In a white petticoat,

And a red nose;

The longer she stands

The shorter she grows.

SYNOPSIS

The poem is a riddle. The poem's title is the answer. Nanny Etticoat is a candle (white petticoat) with a red flame (nose). The candle grows shorter the longer it burns.

ENRICHMENT ACTIVITIES

1. **Recite Poem Information**
   Practice reciting the title of the poem and the name of the poet.

2. **Narrate the Poem**
   Narrate the poem events or meaning aloud using your own words.

3. **Study the Poem Picture**
   Study the poem picture, and describe how it relates to the poem.

4. **Can You Find It?**
   Find the following in the poem picture: candle wax, candlestick, flame, and snuffer.

5. **Act Out the Poem**
   - As you recite the poem, wave your arms over your head to simulate a flickering candle flame.
   - As you burn, bend your arms as you grow shorter and shorter.

6. **Create Novel Artwork Based on the Poem**
   - One day this week, create artwork of a flickering flame.
   - Use paints, crayons, pastels, Legos, blocks, or Play-Doh to create the artwork.

7. **Explore Rhyming**
   Find and recite the rhyming words in the poem.

VOCABULARY

Students Recite Words	Instructors Read Definitions to Students
petticoat	A type of ornamental skirt or underskirt, often displayed below a dress.
longer	A greater duration.
shorter	A smaller distance from one end or edge to another.
grows	Becomes larger.

REVIEW QUESTIONS

1. What is the title of the poem?

2. What happens in the poem?

3. Who are the characters in the poem?

4. Describe the poem picture.

TRACEWORK AND/OR COPYWORK

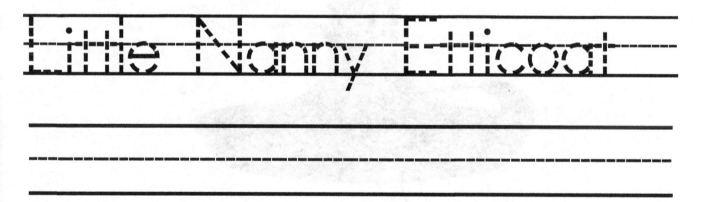

COLOR THE POEM

LESSON 28: "CURLY-LOCKS"

FEATURED POEM

Curly-locks, Curly-locks, wilt thou be mine?

Thou shalt not wash the dishes, nor yet feed the swine;

But sit on a cushion, and sew a fine seam

And feed upon strawberries, sugar, and cream.

SYNOPSIS

The narrator asks Curly-locks to be his and promises her a leisurely life of sitting on cushions and eating strawberries and cream.

ENRICHMENT ACTIVITIES

1. **Recite Poem Information**
   Practice reciting the title of the poem and the name of the poet.

2. **Narrate the Poem**
   Narrate the poem events or meaning aloud using your own words.

3. **Study the Poem Picture**
   Study the poem picture, and describe how it relates to the poem.

4. **Can You Find It?**
   Find the following in the poem picture: Curly-locks, bonnet, bird, bird stand, strawberries, needle and thread, and screen.

5. **Act Out the Poem**
   • As you recite the poem, pretend to be Curly-Locks living a life of leisure.
   • Pretend to sew and eat strawberries and cream.

6. **Create Novel Artwork Based on the Poem**
   • One day this week, create artwork of a bowl of strawberries and cream.
   • Use paints, crayons, pastels, Legos, blocks, or Play-Doh to create the artwork.

7. **Explore Rhyming**
   Find and recite the rhyming words in the poem.

VOCABULARY

Students Recite Words	Instructors Read Definitions to Students
wilt	Archaic form of *will*.
thou	Archaic form of *you*.
shalt	Archaic form of *shall*.
swine	Pigs.
seam	The stitching that joins two or more pieces of fabric.

REVIEW QUESTIONS

1. What is the title of the poem?

2. What happens in the poem?

3. Who are the characters in the poem?

4. Describe the poem picture.

TRACEWORK AND/OR COPYWORK

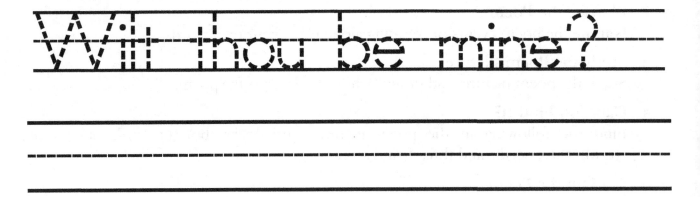

COLOR THE POEM

LESSON 29: "HUMPTY DUMPTY"

FEATURED POEM

Humpty Dumpty sat on a wall,

Humpty Dumpty had a great fall;

All the King's horses, and all the King's men

Cannot put Humpty Dumpty together again.

SYNOPSIS

The poem is a riddle, and an egg is the answer. In the poem, an egg named Humpty Dumpty falls, breaks, and cannot be fixed.

ENRICHMENT ACTIVITIES

1. **Recite Poem Information**
   Practice reciting the title of the poem and the name of the poet.

2. **Narrate the Poem**
   Narrate the poem events or meaning aloud using your own words.

3. **Study the Poem Picture**
   Study the poem picture, and describe how it relates to the poem.

4. **Can You Find It?**
   Find the following in the poem picture: Humpty Dumpty, wall, bird house, birds, something falling, bow tie, and egg.

5. **Act Out the Poem**
   As you recite the poem, wobble in your chair like Humpty wobbling on the wall.

6. **Create Novel Artwork Based on the Poem**
   - One day this week, create artwork of a cracked egg.
   - Use paints, crayons, pastels, Legos, blocks, or Play-Doh to create the artwork.

7. **Explore Rhyming**
   Find and recite the rhyming words in the poem.

VOCABULARY

Students Recite Words	Instructors Read Definitions to Students
wall	A structure built for defense or privacy surrounding a city, castle, yard, etc.
fall	The act of moving to a lower position under the effect of gravity.
cannot	Are unable to.

REVIEW QUESTIONS

1. What is the title of the poem?

2. What happens in the poem?

3. What is the setting of the poem?

4. Who are the characters in the poem?

5. Does the poem teach us anything?

6. Describe the poem picture.

TRACEWORK AND/OR COPYWORK

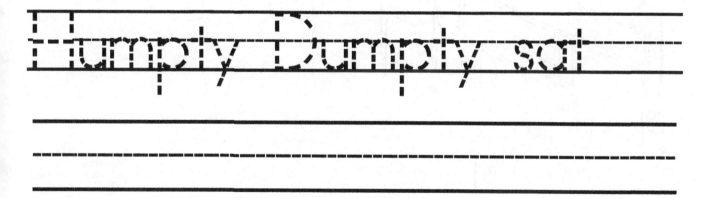

COLOR THE POEM

LESSON 30: "PINS"

FEATURED POEM

See a pin and pick it up,

All the day you'll have good luck.

See a pin and let it lay,

Bad luck you'll have all the day.

SYNOPSIS

The poem advises the reader to *waste not, want not*, even if it is only a pin on the floor.

ENRICHMENT ACTIVITIES

1. **Recite Poem Information**
   Practice reciting the title of the poem and the name of the poet.

2. **Narrate the Poem**
   Narrate the poem events or meaning aloud using your own words.

3. **Study the Poem Picture**
   Study the poem picture, and describe how it relates to the poem.

4. **Can You Find It?**
   Find the following in the poem picture: mother, baby, wheeled toy, string, broom, bonnet, and finger pointing at a pin.

5. **Act Out the Poem**
   - Place a few paperclips, squares of paper, pennies, or other small objects on your table or desk.
   - As you recite the poem, pick up the objects.

6. **Create Novel Artwork Based on the Poem**
   - One day this week, create artwork of a pile of pins.
   - Use paints, crayons, pastels, Legos, blocks, or Play-Doh to create the artwork.

7. **Explore Rhyming**
   Find and recite the rhyming words in the poem.

VOCABULARY

Students Recite Words	Instructors Read Definitions to Students
pin	A small thin piece of metal with a wider head and a sharp point.
pick	To grasp and pull with the fingers or fingernails.
luck	A superstitious feeling that brings fortune or success (good luck) or misfortune and failure (bad luck).
lay	At rest in a horizontal position.

REVIEW QUESTIONS

1. What is the title of the poem?

2. What happens in the poem?

3. Does the poem teach us anything?

4. Describe the poem picture.

TRACEWORK AND/OR COPYWORK

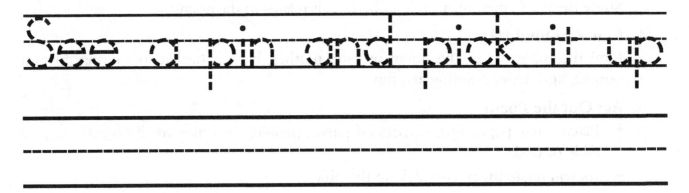

COLOR THE POEM

LESSON 31: "THE MOUSE AND THE CLOCK"

FEATURED POEM

Hickory, dickory, dock!

The mouse ran up the clock;

The clock struck one,

And down he run,

Hickory, dickory, dock!

SYNOPSIS

A mouse runs up a clock. When the clock gongs at one o'clock, the mouse runs back down.

ENRICHMENT ACTIVITIES

1. **Recite Poem Information**
   Practice reciting the title of the poem and the name of the poet.

2. **Narrate the Poem**
   Narrate the poem events or meaning aloud using your own words.

3. **Study the Poem Picture**
   Study the poem picture, and describe how it relates to the poem.

4. **Can You Find It?**
   Find the following in the poem picture: clock, clock hands, clock face, clock pendulum, clock weights, mouse, stool, and girl.

5. **Act Out the Poem**
   As you recite the poem, use your hand (mouse) to mimic climbing up and down a pretend clock.

6. **Create Novel Artwork Based on the Poem**
   - One day this week, create artwork of a startled or surprised mouse.
   - Use paints, crayons, pastels, Legos, blocks, or Play-Doh to create the artwork.

7. **Explore Rhyming**
   Find and recite the rhyming words in the poem.

VOCABULARY

Students Recite Words	Instructors Read Definitions to Students
hickory	Of or pertaining to the hickory tree or its wood.
clock	An instrument used to measure or keep track of time.
struck	Announced an hour of the day, usually by one or more sounds.

REVIEW QUESTIONS

1. What is the title of the poem?

2. What happens in the poem?

3. What is the setting of the poem?

4. Who are the characters in the poem?

5. Does the poem teach us anything?

6. Describe the poem picture.

TRACEWORK AND/OR COPYWORK

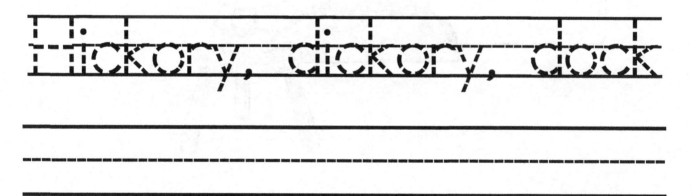

COLOR THE POEM

LESSON 32: "JACK JELF"

FEATURED POEM

Little Jack Jelf

Was put on the shelf

Because he could not spell "pie;"

When his aunt, Mrs. Grace,

Saw his sorrowful face,

She could not help saying, "Oh, fie!"

And since Master Jelf

Was put on the shelf

Because he could not spell "pie,"

Let him stand there so grim,

And no more about him,

For I wish him a very good-bye!

SYNOPSIS

A boy is placed on a shelf due to his difficulties with spelling. He cannot spell *pie*.

ENRICHMENT ACTIVITIES

1. **Recite Poem Information**
   Practice reciting the title of the poem and the name of the poet.

2. **Narrate the Poem**
   Narrate the poem events or meaning aloud using your own words.

3. **Study the Poem Picture**
   Study the poem picture, and describe how it relates to the poem.

4. **Can You Find It?**
   Find the following in the poem picture: Jack Jelf, shelf, shoes, hose, and someone who cannot spell *pie*.

5. **Act Out the Poem**
   - Teach Jack how to spell *pie* so he can leave the shelf.
   - Practice reciting, "P, I, E spells *pie*."

6. **Create Novel Artwork Based on the Poem**
   - One day this week, draw or paint a pie. Label the picture with the word *PIE*.
   - Use paints, crayons, or pastels to create the artwork.

7. **Explore Rhyming**
   Find and recite the rhyming words in the poem.

8. **Discuss the Poem**
   - Do you think it was right for Jack Jelf to be left on a shelf? Explain why or why not.
   - Would you have helped Jack off the shelf? Explain why or why not.

VOCABULARY

Students Recite Words	Instructors Read Definitions to Students
shelf	A projecting ledge used to support, store, or display objects.
spell	To write or say the letters that form a word or part of a word.
sorrowful	Sad, dejected, or distraught.
fie	An expression used to communicate dismay, distaste, or outrage.
grim	Dismal and gloomy.

REVIEW QUESTIONS

1. What is the title of the poem?
2. What happens in the poem?
3. What is the setting of the poem?
4. Who are the characters in the poem?
5. Describe the poem picture.

TRACEWORK AND/OR COPYWORK

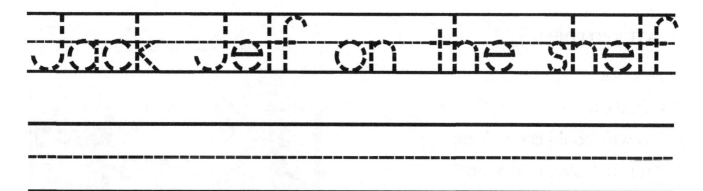

COLOR THE POEM

LESSON 33: "JACK SPRAT"

FEATURED POEM

Jack Sprat

Could eat no fat,

His wife could eat no lean;

And so, betwixt them both,

They licked the platter clean.

SYNOPSIS

The poem remarks on the cooperation between a husband and a wife. One eats fat, the other lean, and together they eat everything and waste nothing.

ENRICHMENT ACTIVITIES

1. **Recite Poem Information**
   Practice reciting the title of the poem and the name of the poet.

2. **Narrate the Poem**
   Narrate the poem events or meaning aloud using your own words.

3. **Study the Poem Picture**
   Study the poem picture, and describe how it relates to the poem.

4. **Can You Find It?**
   Find the following in the poem picture: Jack Sprat, Jack Sprat's wife, cat, rug, plates, cup, saucer, bowl, spoon, serving platter, fat, lean, and tablecloth.

5. **Act Out the Poem**
   As you recite the poem, pretend to say no to either fat or lean and lick the platter clean.

6. **Create Novel Artwork Based on the Poem**
   - One day this week, create artwork that shows two people sharing something, perhaps a toy or an ice cream cone.
   - Use paints, crayons, pastels, Legos, blocks, or Play-Doh to create the artwork.

7. **Explore Rhyming**
   Find and recite the rhyming words in the poem.

VOCABULARY

Students Recite Words	Instructors Read Definitions to Students
fat	The fatty part of meat.
lean	Meat having little fat.
betwixt	Archaic word for *between*.
platter	A tray for serving foods.

REVIEW QUESTIONS

1. What is the title of the poem?

2. What happens in the poem?

3. What is the setting of the poem?

4. Who are the characters in the poem?

5. Does the poem teach us anything?

6. Describe the poem picture.

TRACEWORK AND/OR COPYWORK

COLOR THE POEM

LESSON 34: "HUSH-A-BYE"

FEATURED POEM

Hush-a-bye, baby, lie still with thy daddy,

Thy mammy has gone to the mill,

To get some meal to bake a cake,

So pray, my dear baby, lie still.

SYNOPSIS

A daddy cares for his baby. He recites a poem to calm the baby.

ENRICHMENT ACTIVITIES

1. **Recite Poem Information**
   Practice reciting the title of the poem and the name of the poet.

2. **Narrate the Poem**
   Narrate the poem events or meaning aloud using your own words.

3. **Study the Poem Picture**
   Study the poem picture, and describe how it relates to the poem.

4. **Can You Find It?**
   Find the following in the poem picture: the daddy, the baby, cradle, fist, pillow, and stool.

5. **Act Out the Poem**
   As you recite the poem, pretend to hold and rock a baby in your arms.

6. **Create Novel Artwork Based on the Poem**
   - One day this week, create artwork of a crying baby.
   - Use paints, crayons, pastels, Legos, blocks, or Play-Doh to create the artwork.

7. **Explore Rhyming**
   Find and recite the rhyming words in the poem.

VOCABULARY

Students Recite Words	Instructors Read Definitions to Students
hush	To make or become quiet.
still	Not moving.
thy	Archaic version of *your*.
mammy	Mommy or mamma.
mill	A place that grinds substances such as grains or seeds.
meal	The coarse-ground edible part of various grains often used to feed animals; flour or a coarser blend than flour.
pray	To petition or solicit help from a supernatural or higher being.

REVIEW QUESTIONS

1. What is the title of the poem?

2. What happens in the poem?

3. What is the setting of the poem?

4. Who are the characters in the poem?

5. Describe the poem picture.

TRACEWORK AND/OR COPYWORK

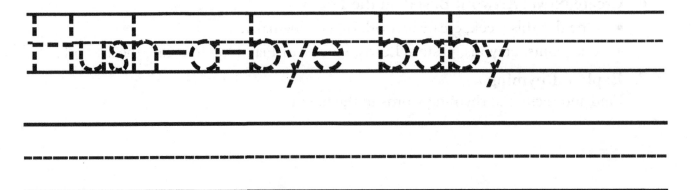

COLOR THE POEM

LESSON 35: "NANCY DAWSON"

FEATURED POEM

Nancy Dawson was so fine

She wouldn't get up to serve the swine;

She lies in bed till eight or nine,

So it's Oh, poor Nancy Dawson.

And do ye ken Nancy Dawson, honey?

The wife who sells the barley, honey?

She won't get up to feed her swine,

And do ye ken Nancy Dawson, honey?

SYNOPSIS

Nancy Dawson lies in bed and does not work. Nancy Dawson was a real person, a dancer, who lived in the 1700s. She achieved fame for her dancing. There are multiple references to her in poetry and literature.

ENRICHMENT ACTIVITIES

1. **Recite Poem Information**
   Practice reciting the title of the poem and the name of the poet.

2. **Narrate the Poem**
   Narrate the poem events or meaning aloud using your own words.

3. **Study the Poem Picture**
   Study the poem picture, and describe how it relates to the poem.

4. **Can You Find It?**
   Find the following in the poem picture: Nancy Dawson, four-poster bed, window, curtains, comforter, bed skirt, nightcap, and pillow.

5. **Act Out the Poem**
   - Pretend to be Nancy Dawson.
   - As you recite the poem, lay your head on your hands and pretend to refuse to get up.

6. **Create Novel Artwork Based on the Poem**
   - One day this week, build a four-poster bed out of Legos, blocks, or Play-Doh.
   - Don't forget the pillow.

7. **Explore Rhyming**
   Find and recite the rhyming words in the poem.

VOCABULARY

Students Recite Words	Instructors Read Definitions to Students
fine	Delicate or refined.
swine	Pigs.
ye	Archaic form of *you*.
ken	Archaic form of *know*.
honey	A term of affection similar to dear or sweetie.
barley	A cereal often used as food or to make beer and other malted drinks.

REVIEW QUESTIONS

1. What is the title of the poem?

2. What happens in the poem?

3. Who are the characters in the poem?

4. Does the poem teach us anything?

5. Describe the poem picture.

TRACEWORK AND/OR COPYWORK

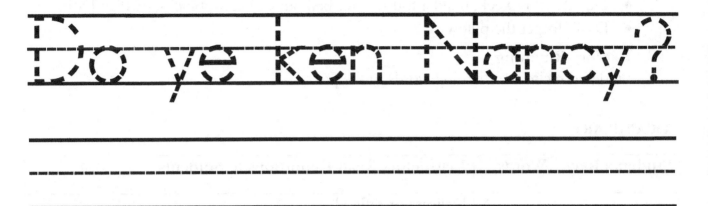

COLOR THE POEM

LESSON 36: "THE ALPHABET"

FEATURED POEM

A, B, C, and D,

Pray, playmates, agree.

E, F, and G,

Well, so it shall be.

J, K, and L,

In peace we will dwell.

M, N, and O,

To play let us go.

P, Q, R, and S,

Love may we possess.

W, X, and Y,

Will not quarrel or die.

Z, and ampersand,

Go to school at command.

SYNOPSIS

This poem is to be read or recited aloud for learning the alphabet.

ENRICHMENT ACTIVITIES

1. **Recite Poem Information**
   Practice reciting the title of the poem and the name of the poet.

2. **Narrate the Poem**
   Narrate the poem events or meaning aloud using your own words.

3. **Study the Poem Picture**
   Study the poem picture, and describe how it relates to the poem.

4. **Can You Find It?**
   Find the following in the poem picture: girl, blocks, ampersand (&), dolly, book, drapes, and window.

5. **Act Out the Poem**
   - As you recite the poem, contort your arms into as many of the letters as you can.
   - For example, make a triangle with your fingers to form an "A" with your hands and arms.

6. **Create Novel Artwork Based on the Poem**
   One day this week, use Legos, blocks, or Play-Doh to create sculptures of three alphabet letters.

7. **Explore Rhyming**
   Find and recite the rhyming words in the poem.

VOCABULARY

Students Recite Words	Instructors Read Definitions to Students
peace	A state of quiet, free from conflict or war.
dwell	To live; to reside.
possess	To have; to own.
quarrel	A verbal dispute or argument.
ampersand	The symbol & pronounced *and*.
command	An order to do something.

REVIEW QUESTIONS

1. What is the title of the poem?
2. What happens in the poem?
3. Does the poem teach us anything?
4. Describe the poem picture.

TRACEWORK AND/OR COPYWORK

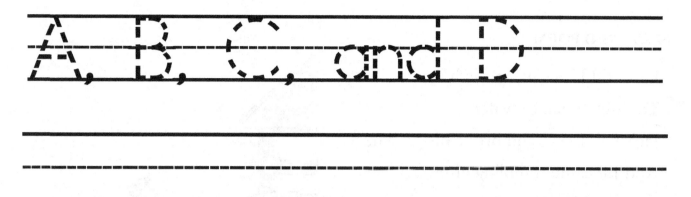

COLOR THE POEM

LESSON 37: "JACK AND JILL"

FEATURED POEM

Jack and Jill went up the hill,

To fetch a pail of water;

Jack fell down, and broke his crown,

And Jill came tumbling after.

Then up Jack got and off did trot,

As fast as he could caper,

To old Dame Dob, who patched his nob

With vinegar and brown paper.

SYNOPSIS

Jack and Jill fall down a hill while trying to get water from a well. Jack runs to Dame Dob to fix his hurt head.

ENRICHMENT ACTIVITIES

1. **Recite Poem Information**
   Practice reciting the title of the poem and the name of the poet.

2. **Narrate the Poem**
   Narrate the poem events or meaning aloud using your own words.

3. **Study the Poem Picture**
   Study the poem picture, and describe how it relates to the poem.

4. **Can You Find It?**
   Find the following in the poem picture: Jack, Jill, stones, well, hand crank, bucket, and hill.

5. **Act Out the Poem**
   - As you recite the poem, pretend your hands are Jack and Jill and use your finger-legs to climb up the hill.
   - Flutter your fingers and lower your hands as Jack or Jill fall down the hill.

6. **Create Novel Artwork Based on the Poem**
   - One day this week, create artwork of a well.
   - Use paints, crayons, pastels, Legos, blocks, or Play-Doh to create the artwork.

7. **Explore Rhyming**
Find and recite the rhyming words in the poem.

VOCABULARY

Students Recite Words	Instructors Read Definitions to Students
pail	A vessel of wood, tin, plastic, etc., usually cylindrical and having a handle.
crown	The topmost part of the head.
caper	To leap or jump about in a sprightly manner.
nob	The head.
vinegar	A sour liquid used as a condiment or preservative

REVIEW QUESTIONS

1. What is the title of the poem?

2. What happens in the poem?

3. What is the setting of the poem?

4. Who are the characters in the poem?

5. Does the poem teach us anything?

6. Describe the poem picture.

TRACEWORK AND/OR COPYWORK

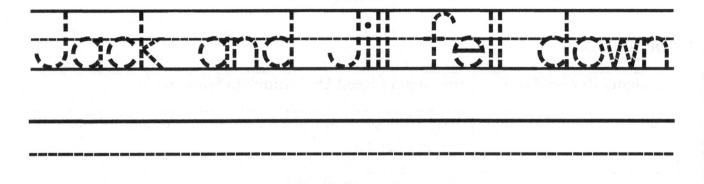

COLOR THE POEM

LESSON 38: "DANCE TO YOUR DADDY"

FEATURED POEM

Dance to your daddie,

My bonnie laddie;

Dance to your daddie, my bonnie lamb;

You shall get a fishy,

On a little dishy;

You shall get a fishy, when the boat comes home.

SYNOPSIS

A woman tells a boy to greet his father by dancing when his father returns from a fishing trip.

ENRICHMENT ACTIVITIES

1. **Recite Poem Information**
   Practice reciting the title of the poem and the name of the poet.

2. **Narrate the Poem**
   Narrate the poem events or meaning aloud using your own words.

3. **Study the Poem Picture**
   Study the poem picture, and describe how it relates to the poem.

4. **Can You Find It?**
   Find the following in the poem picture: mother, baby, apron, sea, beach, and starfish.

5. **Act Out the Poem**
   Dance a little in your chair while reciting this poem.

6. **Create Novel Artwork Based on the Poem**
   - One day this week, create artwork of a fish on a dish.
   - Use paints, crayons, pastels, Legos, blocks, or Play-Doh to create the artwork.

7. **Explore Rhyming**
   Find and recite the rhyming words in the poem.

VOCABULARY

Students Recite Words	Instructors Read Definitions to Students
daddie	Alternate spelling of *daddy*.
bonnie	Merry; good; beautiful.
laddie	A small boy.

REVIEW QUESTIONS

1. What is the title of the poem?

2. What happens in the poem?

3. Who are the characters in the poem?

4. How do we know the poem refers to a son and not a daughter?

5. Describe the poem picture.

TRACEWORK AND/OR COPYWORK

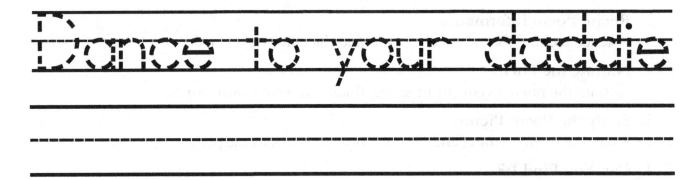

COLOR THE POEM

LESSON 39: "ONE MISTY MOISTY MORNING"

FEATURED POEM

One misty moisty morning,

When cloudy was the weather,

I chanced to meet an old man,

Clothed all in leather.

He began to compliment

And I began to grin.

How do you do? And how do you do?

And how do you do again?

SYNOPSIS

A girl meets an older man. She smiles when he compliments her.

ENRICHMENT ACTIVITIES

1. **Recite Poem Information**
   Practice reciting the title of the poem and the name of the poet.

2. **Narrate the Poem**
   Narrate the poem events or meaning aloud using your own words.

3. **Study the Poem Picture**
   Study the poem picture, and describe how it relates to the poem.

4. **Can You Find It?**
   Find the following in the poem picture: girl, umbrella, older man, and cane.

5. **Act Out the Poem**
   - Practice giving people compliments.
   - Tell someone good job for something, or tell someone they look nice.

6. **Create Novel Artwork Based on the Poem**
   - One day this week, create artwork of a cloudy, misty day.
   - Use paints, crayons, pastels, Legos, blocks, or Play-Doh to create the artwork.

7. **Explore Rhyming**
   Find and recite the rhyming words in the poem.

VOCABULARY

Students Recite Words	Instructors Read Definitions to Students
misty	With fine droplets of water suspended in the air; foggy.
moisty	Slightly wet; damp.
leather	A tough material produced from the skin of animals.
compliment	An expression of praise, congratulation, encouragement, or respect.
grin	A smile in which the lips are parted to reveal the teeth.

REVIEW QUESTIONS

1. What is the title of the poem?

2. What happens in the poem?

3. What is the setting of the poem?

4. Who are the characters in the poem?

5. Does the poem teach us anything?

6. Describe the poem picture.

TRACEWORK AND/OR COPYWORK

COLOR THE POEM

LESSON 40: "THE OLD WOMAN FROM FRANCE"

FEATURED POEM

There came an old woman from France

Who taught grown-up children to dance;

But they were so stiff,

She sent them home in a sniff,

This sprightly old woman from France.

SYNOPSIS

An old woman tries to teach children to dance. When the children are too stiff, she sends them home.

ENRICHMENT ACTIVITIES

1. **Recite Poem Information**
   Practice reciting the title of the poem and the name of the poet.

2. **Narrate the Poem**
   Narrate the poem events or meaning aloud using your own words.

3. **Study the Poem Picture**
   Study the poem picture, and describe how it relates to the poem.

4. **Can You Find It?**
   Find the following in the poem picture: someone from France, students, and candles.

5. **Act Out the Poem**
   - Use your hands to play the roles of teacher and student.
   - As you recite the poem, act out the teacher showing the student a dance step.

6. **Create Novel Artwork Based on the Poem**
   - One day this week, create artwork of two people dancing.
   - Use paints, crayons, pastels, Legos, blocks, or Play-Doh to create the artwork.

7. **Explore Rhyming**
   Find and recite the rhyming words in the poem.

VOCABULARY

Students Recite Words	Instructors Read Definitions to Students
France	A country in Western Europe.
grown-up	An adult.
stiff	Hard to bend.
sniff	A noise made by quickly breathing in through the nose.
sprightly	Full of life and energetic.

REVIEW QUESTIONS

1. What is the title of the poem?

2. What happens in the poem?

3. What is the setting of the poem?

4. Who are the characters in the poem?

5. Describe the poem picture.

TRACEWORK AND/OR COPYWORK

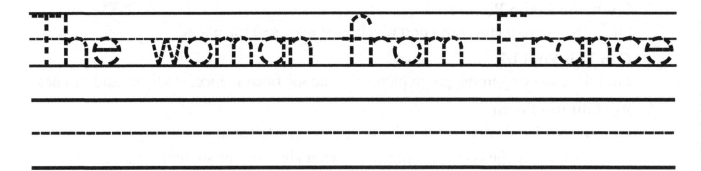

COLOR THE POEM

LESSON 41: "MY KITTEN"

FEATURED POEM

Hey, my kitten, my kitten,

And hey, my kitten, my deary!

Such a sweet pet as this

Was neither far nor neary.

SYNOPSIS

The narrator says an ode to their beloved kitten.

ENRICHMENT ACTIVITIES

1. **Recite Poem Information**
   Practice reciting the title of the poem and the name of the poet.

2. **Narrate the Poem**
   Narrate the poem events or meaning aloud using your own words.

3. **Study the Poem Picture**
   Study the poem picture, and describe how it relates to the poem.

4. **Can You Find It?**
   Find the following in the poem picture: woman, kitten, yarn, apron, footrest, sock, bird cage, curtains, and flower pot.

5. **Act Out the Poem**
   - The narrator says an ode (poem expressing love or admiration) to their kitten, because they love their kitten.
   - Think of something you love.
   - Make up and recite an ode to the thing you love.

6. **Create Novel Artwork Based on the Poem**
   - One day this week, create artwork of the thing you love the most.
   - Use paints, crayons, pastels, Legos, blocks, or Play-Doh to create the artwork.

7. **Explore Rhyming**
   Find and recite the rhyming words in the poem.

VOCABULARY

Students Recite Words	Instructors Read Definitions to Students
deary	A sweetie or a darling.
sweet	Very pleasing; kind; agreeable.
neither	Not one of two; not either.
far	Distant in space.
near	Close by.

REVIEW QUESTIONS

1. What is the title of the poem?

2. What happens in the poem?

3. Who are the characters in the poem?

4. Describe the poem picture.

TRACEWORK AND/OR COPYWORK

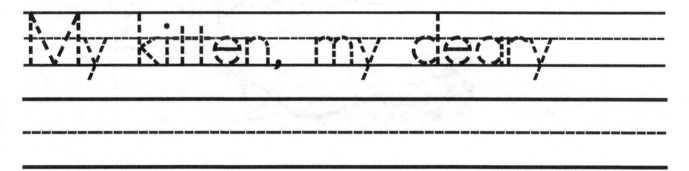

COLOR THE POEM

LESSON 42: "PANCAKE DAY"

FEATURED POEM

Great A, little a,

This is pancake day;

Toss the ball high,

Throw the ball low,

Those that come after

May sing heigh-ho!

SYNOPSIS

Pancake day is a day in Great Britain before Lent, where people make pancakes to use up eggs and milk. The inclusion of ball throwing suggests children playing catch might recite the poem in rhythm with the toss of the ball.

ENRICHMENT ACTIVITIES

1. **Recite Poem Information**
   Practice reciting the title of the poem and the name of the poet.

2. **Narrate the Poem**
   Narrate the poem events or meaning aloud using your own words.

3. **Study the Poem Picture**
   Study the poem picture, and describe how it relates to the poem.

4. **Can You Find It?**
   Find the following in the poem picture: girl, boy, dog, ball, bonnet, hill, and clouds.

5. **Act Out the Poem**
   - In a safe place, play catch with a soft, foam ball or crumpled piece of paper while reciting the poem.
   - Throw the ball high and roll the ball low along with the poem.

6. **Create Novel Artwork Based on the Poem**
   - One day this week, create artwork of a large stack of pancakes. Add syrup and butter if you wish.
   - Use paints, crayons, pastels, Legos, blocks, or Play-Doh to create the artwork.

7. **Explore Rhyming**
   Find and recite the rhyming words in the poem.

VOCABULARY

Students Recite Words	Instructors Read Definitions to Students
pancake	A thin batter cake fried in a pan in oil or butter.
toss	A throw or a lob of a ball, particularly with a lack of care.
high	Very elevated.
low	Situated not far above.
after	Behind; later in time; following.
sing	To produce musical or harmonious sounds with one's voice.

REVIEW QUESTIONS

1. What is the title of the poem?

2. What happens in the poem?

3. Describe the poem picture.

TRACEWORK AND/OR COPYWORK

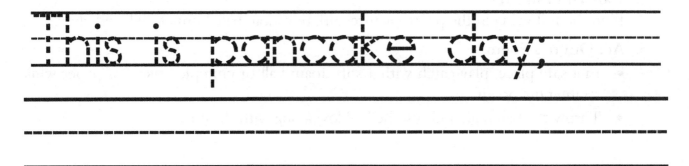

COLOR THE POEM

LESSON 43: "THE MERCHANTS OF LONDON"

FEATURED POEM

Hey diddle dinkety poppety pet,

The merchants of London they wear scarlet,

Silk in the collar and gold in the hem,

So merrily march the merchant men.

SYNOPSIS

The poem discusses the fancy dress of the merchants of London.

ENRICHMENT ACTIVITIES

1. **Recite Poem Information**
   Practice reciting the title of the poem and the name of the poet.

2. **Narrate the Poem**
   Narrate the poem events or meaning aloud using your own words.

3. **Study the Poem Picture**
   Study the poem picture, and describe how it relates to the poem.

4. **Can You Find It?**
   Find the following in the poem picture: merchants, collars, coats, buttons, glasses, banner, and walking stick.

5. **Act Out the Poem**
   - As you recite the poem, march merrily like the merchants of London.
   - Stride about with great importance and nod grandly at your spectators.

6. **Create Novel Artwork Based on the Poem**
   - One day this week, create artwork of one of the merchants of London. Give the merchant brightly colored clothing.
   - Use paints, crayons, pastels, Legos, blocks, or Play-Doh to create the artwork.

7. **Explore Rhyming**
   Find and recite the rhyming words in the poem.

VOCABULARY

Students Recite Words	Instructors Read Definitions to Students
merchant	A person who buys, sells, and trades things to make money.
London	The capital city of the United Kingdom and of England.
scarlet	A vivid red.
silk	A fine fiber excreted by the silkworm or a spider.
hem	The border of an article of clothing doubled back and stitched together to finish the edge and prevent it from fraying.
merrily	In a cheerful manner.
march	A formal, rhythmic way of walking, used especially by soldiers, by bands, and in ceremonies.

REVIEW QUESTIONS

1. What is the title of the poem?

2. What happens in the poem?

3. Who are the characters in the poem?

4. Describe the poem picture.

TRACEWORK AND/OR COPYWORK

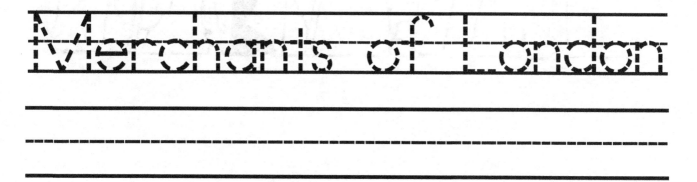

COLOR THE POEM

LESSON 44: "SLEEP BABY SLEEP"

FEATURED POEM

Sleep, baby, sleep,

Our cottage vale is deep:

The little lamb is on the green,

With woolly fleece so soft and clean--

Sleep, baby, sleep.

Sleep, baby, sleep.

Down where the woodbines creep;

Be always like the lamb so mild,

A kind, and sweet, and gentle child.

Sleep, baby, sleep.

SYNOPSIS

The poem is a lullaby. The narrator sings a baby to sleep.

ENRICHMENT ACTIVITIES

1. **Recite Poem Information**
   Practice reciting the title of the poem and the name of the poet.

2. **Narrate the Poem**
   Narrate the poem events or meaning aloud using your own words.

3. **Study the Poem Picture**
   Study the poem picture, and describe how it relates to the poem.

4. **Can You Find It?**
   Find the following in the poem picture: cradle, woman, drapes, and windows.

5. **Act Out the Poem**
   - Use your hands to play the roles of the narrator and the baby.
   - Have one hand recite the poem while the other falls asleep.

6. **Create Novel Artwork Based on the Poem**
   - One day this week, create artwork of a lamb with woolly fleece.
   - Use paints, crayons, pastels, Legos, blocks, or Play-Doh to create the artwork.

7. **Explore Rhyming**
   Find and recite the rhyming words in the poem.

VOCABULARY

Students Recite Words	Instructors Read Definitions to Students
lullaby	A cradlesong, a soothing song to calm children or lull them to sleep.
wooly (woolly)	Made of wool; having a thick, soft texture, as if made of wool.
fleece	Hair or wool of a sheep or similar animal.
cottage	A small house.
vale	A valley; An elongated depression between hills or mountains, often with a river flowing through it.
woodbines	Any of several climbing vines, such as the honeysuckle.
creep	To grow across a surface rather than upwards.

REVIEW QUESTIONS

1. What is the title of the poem?
2. What happens in the poem?
3. What is the setting of the poem?
4. Who are the characters in the poem?
5. Describe the poem picture.

TRACEWORK AND/OR COPYWORK

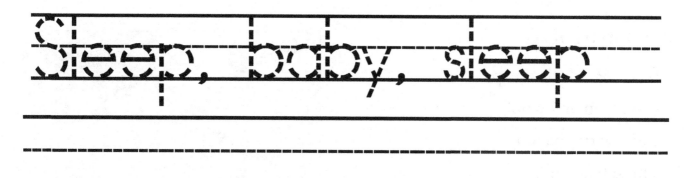

COLOR THE POEM

LESSON 45: "BAA BAA BLACK SHEEP"

FEATURED POEM

Baa, baa, black sheep,

Have you any wool?

Yes, marry, have I,

Three bags full;

One for my master,

One for my dame,

But none for the little boy

Who cries in the lane.

SYNOPSIS

The sheep has wool for his master and his dame, but refuses to give his third bag of wool to a crying boy.

ENRICHMENT ACTIVITIES

1. **Recite Poem Information**
   Practice reciting the title of the poem and the name of the poet.

2. **Narrate the Poem**
   Narrate the poem events or meaning aloud using your own words.

3. **Study the Poem Picture**
   Study the poem picture, and describe how it relates to the poem.

4. **Can You Find It?**
   Find the following in the poem picture: toy, sheep, basket, birdhouse, and rain barrel.

5. **Act Out the Poem**
   - Partner up, and recite the dialog of the main narrator and the sheep.
   - If you are the sheep, give yourself a sheep accent and "baa" a lot.

6. **Create Novel Artwork Based on the Poem**
   - One day this week, create artwork of three bags of wool.
   - Use paints, crayons, pastels, Legos, blocks, or Play-Doh to create the artwork.

7. **Explore Rhyming**
   Find and recite the rhyming words in the poem.

VOCABULARY

Students Recite Words	Instructors Read Definitions to Students
wool	The hair of the sheep.
full	Containing the maximum possible amount of that which can fit.
master	Someone who has control over something or someone.
dame	A lady, a woman.

REVIEW QUESTIONS

1. What is the title of the poem?

2. What happens in the poem?

3. Who are the characters in the poem?

4. Does the poem teach us anything?

5. Describe the poem picture.

TRACEWORK AND/OR COPYWORK

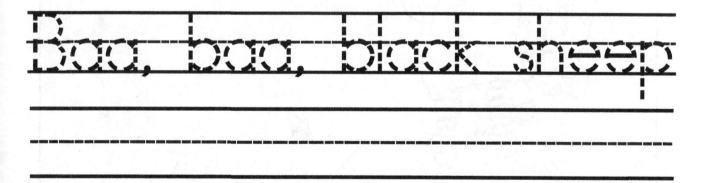

COLOR THE POEM

LESSON 46: "THE CAT AND THE FIDDLE"

FEATURED POEM

Hey, diddle, diddle!

The cat and the fiddle,

The cow jumped over the moon;

The little dog laughed

To see such sport,

And the dish ran away with the
spoon.

SYNOPSIS

The cat has a fiddle, the cow jumps over the moon, the dog laughs, and the dish and spoon
run away.

ENRICHMENT ACTIVITIES

1. **Recite Poem Information**
   Practice reciting the title of the poem and the name of the poet.

2. **Narrate the Poem**
   Narrate the poem events or meaning aloud using your own words.

3. **Study the Poem Picture**
   Study the poem picture, and describe how it relates to the poem.

4. **Can You Find It?**
   Find the following in the poem picture: cat, fiddle, cow, moon, dog, clown outfit, dish,
   and spoon.

5. **Act Out the Poem**
   - While reciting the poem, use your hands to portray jumping over the moon.
   - Laugh like the dog.
   - Use your hands to enact running away like the dish and the spoon.

6. **Create Novel Artwork Based on the Poem**
   - One day this week, create artwork showing a cow jumping over a full moon.
   - Use paints, crayons, pastels, Legos, blocks, or Play-Doh to create the artwork.

7. **Explore Rhyming**
Find and recite the rhyming words in the poem.

VOCABULARY

Students Recite Words	Instructors Read Definitions to Students
fiddle	A stringed instrument played with a bow; a violin.
sport	That which diverts, and makes mirth; pastime; amusement.
dish	A vessel such as a plate for holding or serving food.
spoon	A scooped implement with a long, straight handle for eating or serving.

REVIEW QUESTIONS

1. What is the title of the poem?

2. What happens in the poem?

3. Who are the characters in the poem?

4. Describe the poem picture.

TRACEWORK AND/OR COPYWORK

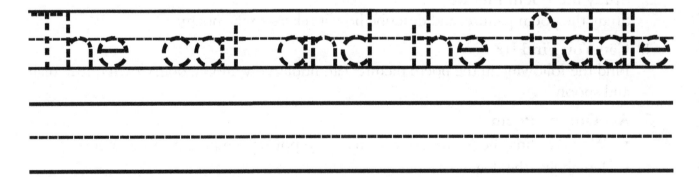

COLOR THE POEM

LESSON 47: "SING A SONG OF SIXPENCE"

FEATURED POEM

Sing a song of sixpence,
A pocket full of rye;
Four-and-twenty blackbirds
Baked in a pie!

When the pie was opened
The birds began to sing;
Was not that a dainty dish
To set before the king?

The king was in his counting-house,
Counting out his money;
The queen was in the parlor,
Eating bread and honey.

The maid was in the garden,
Hanging out the clothes;
When down came a blackbird
And snapped off her nose.

SYNOPSIS

The king is served a pie of live blackbirds and counts his money, the queen eats bread and honey in the parlor, and a blackbird bites a maid on the nose.

ENRICHMENT ACTIVITIES

1. **Recite Poem Information**
   Practice reciting the title of the poem and the name of the poet.

2. **Narrate the Poem**
   Narrate the poem events or meaning aloud using your own words.

3. **Study the Poem Picture**
   Study the poem picture, and describe how it relates to the poem.

4. **Can You Find It?**
   Find the following in the poem picture: king, crown, robe, knife, pie, steam, blackbirds, guard, axe, serving boy, and pitcher.

5. **Act Out the Poem**
   As you recite the poem, pair it with the following hand motions.
   Sing a song of sixpence, **(Cup your mouth with your hands)**
   A pocket full of rye; **(Pat your pocket)**
   Four-and-twenty blackbirds **(Hold up two fingers on one hand, and four on the other)**
   Baked in a pie! **(Hold your hands flat and palms down, with matching middle fingertips touching, like the top of a pie)**

   When the pie was opened **(Open your hands up, like the pie being opened)**
   The birds began to sing; **(Keeping fingers straight, making a talking motion with them)**
   Was not that a dainty dish
   To set before the king? **(Use hands to set an imaginary pie in front the king with a flourish)**

   The king was in his counting-house,
   Counting out his money; **(Pretend to count money with your hands)**
   The queen was in the parlor,
   Eating bread and honey. **(Pretend to spread honey on a piece of bread and eat it)**

   The maid was in the garden,
   Hanging out the clothes; **(Pretend to fasten clothes to a clothesline)**
   When down came a blackbird **(Swoop your hand around like a flying blackbird)**
   And snapped off her nose. **(Gently tweak your own nose)**

6. **Create Novel Artwork Based on the Poem**
   - One day this week, create artwork showing a pie containing live blackbirds.
   - Use paints, crayons, pastels, Legos, blocks, or Play-Doh to create the artwork.

7. **Explore Rhyming**
   Find and recite the rhyming words in the poem.

VOCABULARY

Students Recite Words	Instructors Read Definitions to Students
sixpence	A former British coin.
rye	A grain used extensively in Europe for making bread and beer and as animal fodder.
dainty	Excellent; valuable, fine.
counting-house	An office used by a business to house its accounts department.
parlor	The living room of a house, or a room for entertaining guests.

REVIEW QUESTIONS

1. What is the title of the poem?

2. What happens in the poem?

3. What is the setting of the poem?

4. Who are the characters in the poem?

5. Describe the poem picture.

TRACEWORK AND/OR COPYWORK

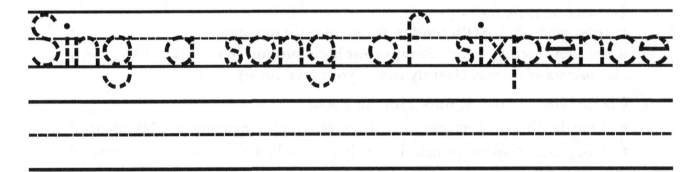

COLOR THE POEM

LESSON 48: "TOMMY TITTLEMOUSE"

FEATURED POEM

Little Tommy Tittlemouse

Lived in a little house;

He caught fishes

In other men's ditches.

SYNOPSIS

Tommy lives in a small house and catches fish where he can, even if it means trespassing.

ENRICHMENT ACTIVITIES

1. **Recite Poem Information**
   Practice reciting the title of the poem and the name of the poet.

2. **Narrate the Poem**
   Narrate the poem events or meaning aloud using your own words.

3. **Study the Poem Picture**
   Study the poem picture, and describe how it relates to the poem.

4. **Can You Find It?**
   Find the following in the poem picture: Tommy Tittlemouse, fishing pole, fishing line, ditch, basket, and *no-trespassing* sign.

5. **Act Out the Poem**
   - Pretend to bait a hook with a worm and drop your line into some water.
   - Pretend reel in a big, heavy fish.

6. **Create Novel Artwork Based on the Poem**
   - One day this week, create artwork of a fish caught on a fishing pole hook.
   - Use paints, crayons, pastels, Legos, blocks, or Play-Doh to create the artwork.

7. **Explore Rhyming**
   Find and recite the rhyming words in the poem.

VOCABULARY

Students Recite Words	Instructors Read Definitions to Students
caught	Seized or captured.
fishes	A cold-blooded vertebrate animal that lives in water, moving with the help of fins and breathing with gills.
ditches	Trenches; long, shallow indentations, as for irrigation or drainage.

REVIEW QUESTIONS

1. What is the title of the poem?

2. What happens in the poem?

3. Who are the characters in the poem?

4. Describe the poem picture.

TRACEWORK AND/OR COPYWORK

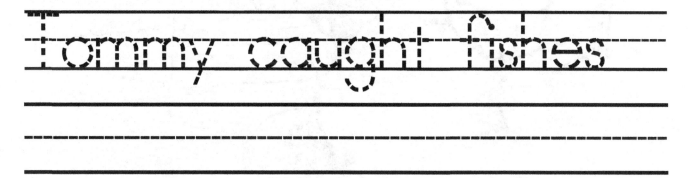

COLOR THE POEM

LESSON 49: "THE HOBBY-HORSE"

FEATURED POEM

I had a little hobby-horse,

And it was dapple gray;

Its head was made of pea-straw,

Its tail was made of hay.

I sold it to an old woman

For a copper groat;

And I'll not sing my song again

Without another coat.

SYNOPSIS

The narrator sells their toy horse to an old woman and later regrets it.

ENRICHMENT ACTIVITIES

1. **Recite Poem Information**
   Practice reciting the title of the poem and the name of the poet.

2. **Narrate the Poem**
   Narrate the poem events or meaning aloud using your own words.

3. **Study the Poem Picture**
   Study the poem picture, and describe how it relates to the poem.

4. **Can You Find It?**
   Find the following in the poem picture: boy, hobby-horse, wheels, feather, string, apron, and lady.

5. **Act Out the Poem**
   - Draw and cut out a coin and toy horse.
   - Find a partner and enact the boy selling his horse and the lady buying the horse.
   - As the boy, act upset and regretful after you sell your horse.

6. **Create Novel Artwork Based on the Poem**
   - One day this week, sketch a still life of one of your toys.
   - Place the toy next to your paper. Look at the toy, and use a pencil to sketch the toy.

7. **Explore Rhyming**
   Find and recite the rhyming words in the poem.

VOCABULARY

Students Recite Words	Instructors Read Definitions to Students
hobby-horse (hobby horse)	A child's toy consisting of a (usually wooden or cloth) horse mounted on a stick.
dapple	An animal with a mottled or spotted skin or coat.
pea-straw	The stalks and leaves of the pea plant.
hay	Grass cut and dried for use as animal fodder.
copper	A reddish-brown metal.
groat	Any of various old coins of England and Scotland.

REVIEW QUESTIONS

1. What is the title of the poem?

2. What happens in the poem?

3. Who are the characters in the poem?

4. Describe the poem picture.

TRACEWORK AND/OR COPYWORK

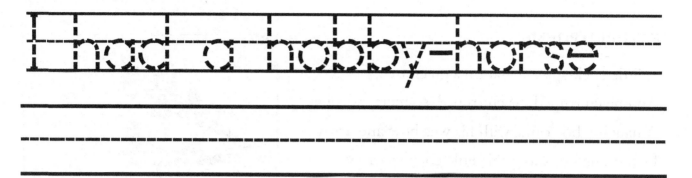

COLOR THE POEM

LESSON 50: "BOY AND THE SPARROW"

FEATURED POEM

A little cock-sparrow sat on a green tree,

And he chirruped, he chirruped, so merry was he;

A naughty boy came with his wee bow and arrow,

Determined to shoot this little cock-sparrow.

"This little cock-sparrow shall make me a stew,

And his giblets shall make me a little pie, too."

"Oh, no," says the sparrow "I won't make a stew."

So he flapped his wings and away he flew.

SYNOPSIS

A boy tries to shoot a sparrow to make stew and pie, but the sparrow escapes.

ENRICHMENT ACTIVITIES

1. **Recite Poem Information**
   Practice reciting the title of the poem and the name of the poet.

2. **Narrate the Poem**
   Narrate the poem events or meaning aloud using your own words.

3. **Study the Poem Picture**
   Study the poem picture, and describe how it relates to the poem.

4. **Can You Find It?**
   Find the following in the poem picture: boy, bow, arrows, bough, and sparrow.

5. **Act Out the Poem**
   - Pretend your hands are the boy and the sparrow.
   - Enact the boy hunting the sparrow and the sparrow escaping.

6. **Create Novel Artwork Based on the Poem**
   - One day this week, create artwork of a bow and arrows.
   - Use paints, crayons, pastels, Legos, blocks, or Play-Doh to create the artwork.

7. **Explore Rhyming**
   Find and recite the rhyming words in the poem.

VOCABULARY

Students Recite Words	Instructors Read Definitions to Students
cock-sparrow	A male sparrow; a small male bird with a short bill, and brown, white and gray feathers.
chirruped	Made sounds including chirps, clicks, or clucks.
merry	Jolly and full of high spirits.
naughty	Mischievous; tending to misbehave or act badly.
wee	Small, little, or tiny.
bow	A weapon made of a curved piece of wood or other flexible material whose ends are connected by a string, used for shooting arrows.
arrow	A thin shaft with a sharp point and a finned tail that is shot from a bow.
stew	A casserole or hotpot of vegetables and/or meat cooked until tender.
giblets	The edible internal organs of a bird, such as the liver or heart.

REVIEW QUESTIONS

1. What is the title of the poem?

2. What happens in the poem?

3. What is the setting of the poem?

4. Who are the characters in the poem?

5. Describe the poem picture.

TRACEWORK AND/OR COPYWORK

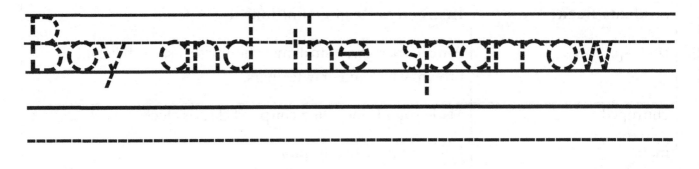

COLOR THE POEM

LESSON 51: "OLD WOMAN, OLD WOMAN"

FEATURED POEM

There was an old woman tossed in a basket,

Seventeen times as high as the moon;

But where she was going no mortal could tell,

For under her arm she carried a broom.

"Old woman, old woman, old woman," said I,

"Whither, oh whither, oh whither so high?"

"To sweep the cobwebs from the sky;

And I'll be with you by-and-by."

SYNOPSIS

A woman in a basket travels higher than the moon to sweep the cobwebs from the sky.

ENRICHMENT ACTIVITIES

1. **Recite Poem Information**
   Practice reciting the title of the poem and the name of the poet.

2. **Narrate the Poem**
   Narrate the poem events or meaning aloud using your own words.

3. **Study the Poem Picture**
   Study the poem picture, and describe how it relates to the poem.

4. **Can You Find It?**
   Find the following in the poem picture: basket, moon, stars, broom, and cape.

5. **Act Out the Poem**
   - Pretend to toss the woman in the basket seventeen times as high as the moon.
   - Enact the old woman sweeping the cobwebs from the sky.

6. **Create Novel Artwork Based on the Poem**
   - One day this week, create artwork of cobwebs.
   - Use paints, crayons, pastels, Legos, blocks, or Play-Doh to create the artwork.

7. **Explore Rhyming**
   Find and recite the rhyming words in the poem.

VOCABULARY

Students Recite Words	Instructors Read Definitions to Students
tossed	Thrown or lobbed, particularly with a lack of care.
basket	A lightweight container, generally round, open at the top, and tapering toward the bottom.
mortal	Human.
whither	To where.
sweep	To clean (a surface) by means of a stroking motion of a broom or brush.
cobwebs	Spiderwebs.

REVIEW QUESTIONS

1. What is the title of the poem?

2. What happens in the poem?

3. What is the setting of the poem?

4. Who are the characters in the poem?

5. Describe the poem picture.

TRACEWORK AND/OR COPYWORK

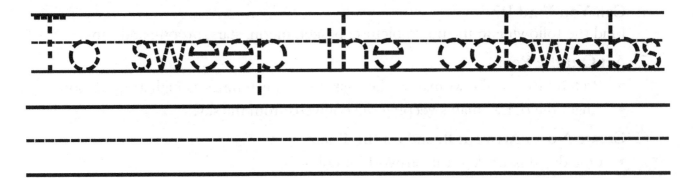

COLOR THE POEM

LESSON 52: "TWO PIGEONS"

FEATURED POEM

I had two pigeons bright and gay,

They flew from me the other day.

What was the reason they did go?

I cannot tell, for I do not know.

SYNOPSIS

Two of the narrator's pigeons fly away for an unknown reason.

ENRICHMENT ACTIVITIES

1. **Recite Poem Information**
   Practice reciting the title of the poem and the name of the poet.

2. **Narrate the Poem**
   Narrate the poem events or meaning aloud using your own words.

3. **Study the Poem Picture**
   Study the poem picture, and describe how it relates to the poem.

4. **Can You Find It?**
   Find the following in the poem picture: girl, sash, bonnet, pan, pigeons, and birdhouse.

5. **Act Out the Poem**
   - As you recite the poem, pretend to feed pigeons some grain.
   - Express dismay when two pigeons go missing, and search for the two missing birds.

6. **Create Novel Artwork Based on the Poem**
   - One day this week, create artwork of a bird house.
   - Use paints, crayons, pastels, Legos, blocks, or Play-Doh to create the artwork.

7. **Explore Rhyming**
   Find and recite the rhyming words in the poem.

VOCABULARY

Students Recite Words	Instructors Read Definitions to Students
pigeon	A large, strong, often gray bird that makes cooing sounds.
reason	That which causes or explains something.
tell	To say; to convey using words.

REVIEW QUESTIONS

1. What is the title of the poem?

2. What happens in the poem?

3. Who are the characters in the poem?

4. Describe the poem picture.

TRACEWORK AND/OR COPYWORK

COLOR THE POEM

LESSON 53: "THE FIRST OF MAY"

FEATURED POEM

The fair maid who, the first of May,

Goes to the fields at break of day,

And washes in dew from the hawthorn-tree,

Will ever after handsome be.

SYNOPSIS

The poem advises that a person who rises early and bathes often will remain healthy and attractive.

ENRICHMENT ACTIVITIES

1. **Recite Poem Information**
   Practice reciting the title of the poem and the name of the poet.

2. **Narrate the Poem**
   Narrate the poem events or meaning aloud using your own words.

3. **Study the Poem Picture**
   Study the poem picture, and describe how it relates to the poem.

4. **Can You Find It?**
   Find the following in the poem picture: maid, sunrise, hawthorn-tree, and bonnet.

5. **Act Out the Poem**
   • As you recite the poem, enact gathering dew from a hawthorn-tree.
   • Pretend to wash your face with the dew.

6. **Create Novel Artwork Based on the Poem**
   • One day this week, create artwork of a hawthorn tree. Draw some dew (water drops) on the leaves.
   • Use paints, crayons, pastels, Legos, blocks, or Play-Doh to create the artwork.

7. **Explore Rhyming**
   Find and recite the rhyming words in the poem.

VOCABULARY

Students Recite Words	Instructors Read Definitions to Students
fair	Lovely, pretty.
maid	A girl or an unmarried young woman.
fields	Lands free of woodland, cities, and towns; open country.
break of day	Dawn, sunrise.
dew	Moisture in the air that settles on plants in the morning, resulting in drops.
hawthorn-tree	Any of various shrubs and small trees having small, apple-like fruits and thorny branches.
handsome	Striking, impressive, and elegantly proportioned, though not typically beautiful.

REVIEW QUESTIONS

1. What is the title of the poem?

2. What happens in the poem?

3. Who are the characters in the poem?

4. Does the poem teach us anything?

5. Describe the poem picture.

TRACEWORK AND/OR COPYWORK

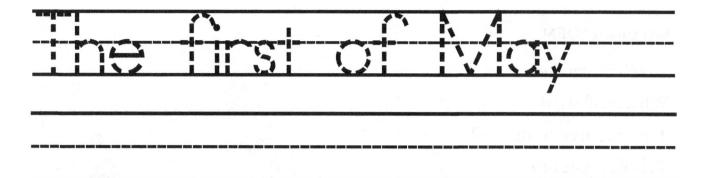

COLOR THE POEM

LESSON 54: "SULKY SUE"

FEATURED POEM

Here's Sulky Sue,

What shall we do?

Turn her face to the wall

Till she comes to.

SYNOPSIS

Sue must face the corner for sulking.

ENRICHMENT ACTIVITIES

1. **Recite Poem Information**
   Practice reciting the title of the poem and the name of the poet.

2. **Narrate the Poem**
   Narrate the poem events or meaning aloud using your own words.

3. **Study the Poem Picture**
   Study the poem picture, and describe how it relates to the poem.

4. **Can You Find It?**
   Find the following in the poem picture: Sulky Sue, dollies, soldier, book, and pointer.

5. **Act Out the Poem**
   - As you recite the poem, pretend to be Sulky Sue.
   - Make a sulky face, and stand in the corner.

6. **Create Novel Artwork Based on the Poem**
   - One day this week, create artwork of a little girl standing in a corner.
   - Use paints, crayons, pastels, Legos, blocks, or Play-Doh to create the artwork.

7. **Explore Rhyming**
   Find and recite the rhyming words in the poem.

VOCABULARY

Students Recite Words	Instructors Read Definitions to Students
sulky	Silent and withdrawn after being upset.
face	To turn so as to have one's face closest to something.

REVIEW QUESTIONS

1. What is the title of the poem?

2. What happens in the poem?

3. Who are the characters in the poem?

4. Does the poem teach us anything?

5. Describe the poem picture.

TRACEWORK AND/OR COPYWORK

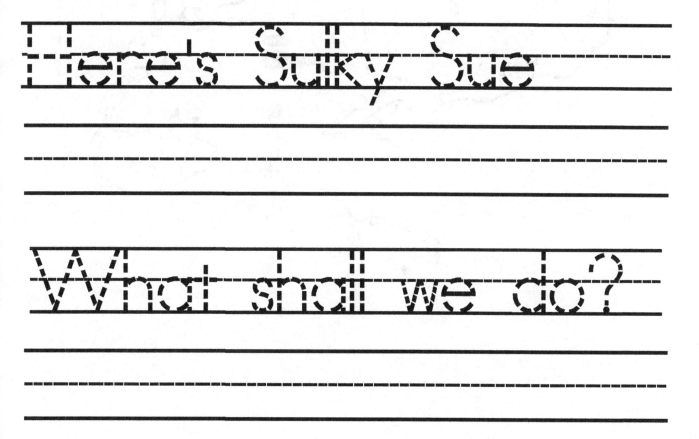

COLOR THE POEM

LESSON 55: "BOBBY SNOOKS"

FEATURED POEM

Little Bobby Snooks was fond of his books,

And loved by his usher and master;

But naughty Jack Spry, he got a black eye,

And carries his nose in a plaster.

SYNOPSIS

Bobby Snooks is a good boy who studies and is loved. Jack Spry gets into trouble and ends up with a black eye and a broken nose.

ENRICHMENT ACTIVITIES

1. **Recite Poem Information**
    Practice reciting the title of the poem and the name of the poet.

2. **Narrate the Poem**
    Narrate the poem events or meaning aloud using your own words.

3. **Study the Poem Picture**
    Study the poem picture, and describe how it relates to the poem.

4. **Can You Find It?**
    Find the following in the poem picture: Jack Spry, books, schoolhouse, eye patch, and nose plaster.

5. **Discuss the Good and Bad Behavior in the Poem**
    - How is Bobby Snooks a good boy?
    - What happens to Jack Spry when he gets into trouble?
    - List some things you can do to be a good person and stay out of trouble.

6. **Explore Rhyming**
    Find and recite the rhyming words in the poem.

VOCABULARY

Students Recite Words	Instructors Read Definitions to Students
fond	Having a liking or affection for.
usher	An archaic term for *schoolteacher*.
naughty	Mischievous; tending to misbehave or act badly.
black eye	An eye which has been bruised and turns a dark color.
plaster	A small adhesive bandage to cover a minor wound.

REVIEW QUESTIONS

1. What is the title of the poem?

2. What happens in the poem?

3. Who are the characters in the poem?

4. Does the poem teach us anything?

5. Describe the poem picture.

TRACEWORK AND/OR COPYWORK

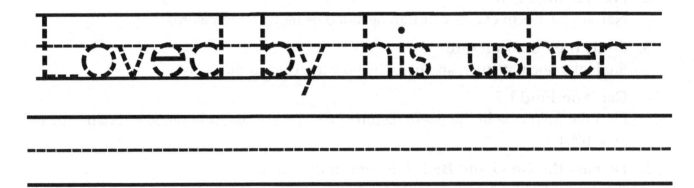

COLOR THE POEM

LESSON 56: "THE MAN IN THE MOON"

FEATURED POEM

The Man in the Moon came tumbling down,

And asked the way to Norwich;

He went by the south, and burnt his mouth

With eating cold pease porridge.

SYNOPSIS

The Man in the Moon falls down, starts for Norwich, and burns his mouth on cold porridge.

ENRICHMENT ACTIVITIES

1. **Recite Poem Information**
   Practice reciting the title of the poem and the name of the poet.

2. **Narrate the Poem**
   Narrate the poem events or meaning aloud using your own words.

3. **Study the Poem Picture**
   Study the poem picture, and describe how it relates to the poem.

4. **Can You Find It?**
   Find the following in the poem picture: Man in the moon, burned mouth, stars, moon, and porridge.

5. **Act Out the Poem**
   As you recite the poem, pretend to burn your mouth while eating cold porridge.

6. **Create Novel Artwork Based on the Poem**
   - One day this week, create artwork of a man living on the moon.
   - Use paints, crayons, pastels, Legos, blocks, or Play-Doh to create the artwork.

7. **Explore Rhyming**
   Find and recite the rhyming words in the poem.

VOCABULARY

Students Recite Words	Instructors Read Definitions to Students
moon	Earth's only natural satellite.
Norwich	A city in England.
south	One of the four major compass points, directed toward the South Pole, conventionally downwards on a map, and abbreviated as S.
burnt	Damaged or injured by fire or heat.
pease porridge	A type of thick soup or stew made from peas.

REVIEW QUESTIONS

1. What is the title of the poem?

2. What happens in the poem?

3. Who are the characters in the poem?

4. Describe the poem picture.

5. Why did the Man in the Moon burn his mouth on cold porridge?

TRACEWORK AND/OR COPYWORK

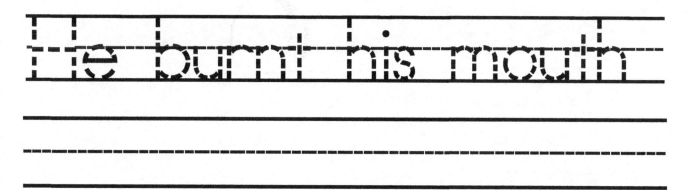

COLOR THE POEM

LESSON 57: "POOR OLD ROBINSON CRUSOE"

FEATURED POEM

Poor old Robinson Crusoe!

Poor old Robinson Crusoe!

They made him a coat

Of an old Nanny goat.

I wonder why they should do so!

With a ring-a-ting-tang,

And a ring-a-ting-tang,

Poor old Robinson Crusoe!

SYNOPSIS

In the poem, Robinson Crusoe wears a coat made of goat's skin. Robinson Crusoe is a literary character who was stranded on a desert island for years.

ENRICHMENT ACTIVITIES

1. **Recite Poem Information**
   Practice reciting the title of the poem and the name of the poet.

2. **Narrate the Poem**
   Narrate the poem events or meaning aloud using your own words.

3. **Study the Poem Picture**
   Study the poem picture, and describe how it relates to the poem.

4. **Can You Find It?**
   Find the following in the poem picture: Robinson Crusoe, coat, gun, sandals, dog, umbrella, palm trees, beach, and the ocean.

5. **Create Novel Artwork Based on the Poem**
   - One day this week, create artwork of a sandy beach and some water.
   - Use paints, crayons, pastels, Legos, blocks, or Play-Doh to create the artwork.

6. **Explore Rhyming**
   Find and recite the rhyming words in the poem.

VOCABULARY

Students Recite Words	Instructors Read Definitions to Students
Robinson Crusoe	A literary character who was stranded on a desert island for years.
coat	An outer garment covering the upper torso and arms.
nanny goat	A female goat.

REVIEW QUESTIONS

1. What is the title of the poem?

2. What happens in the poem?

3. Who are the characters in the poem?

4. Describe the poem picture.

TRACEWORK AND/OR COPYWORK

COLOR THE POEM

LESSON 58: "COCK-CROW"

FEATURED POEM

Cocks crow in the morn

To tell us to rise,

And he who lies late

Will never be wise;

For early to bed

And early to rise,

Is the way to be healthy

And wealthy and wise.

SYNOPSIS

The poem gives advice for successful living - early to bed and early to rise.

ENRICHMENT ACTIVITIES

1. **Recite Poem Information**
   Practice reciting the title of the poem and the name of the poet.

2. **Narrate the Poem**
   Narrate the poem events or meaning aloud using your own words.

3. **Study the Poem Picture**
   Study the poem picture, and describe how it relates to the poem.

4. **Can You Find It?**
   Find the following in the poem picture: someone rising early, bed, open window, bed skirt, and nightshirt.

5. **Create Novel Artwork Based on the Poem**
   - One day this week, create artwork of a rooster crowing at sunrise.
   - Use paints, crayons, pastels, Legos, blocks, or Play-Doh to create the artwork.

6. **Explore Rhyming**
   Find and recite the rhyming words in the poem.

VOCABULARY

Students Recite Words	Instructors Read Definitions to Students
crow	The cry of the rooster.
rise	To leave one's bed; to get up.
wise	Showing good judgement or the benefit of experience.
healthy	Enjoying health and vigor of body, mind, or spirit.
wealthy	Possessing financial wealth; rich.

REVIEW QUESTIONS

1. What is the title of the poem?

2. What happens in the poem?

3. What is the setting of the poem?

4. Who are the characters in the poem?

5. Does the poem teach us anything?

6. Describe the poem picture.

TRACEWORK AND/OR COPYWORK

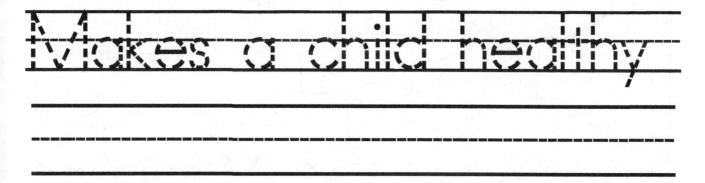

COLOR THE POEM

LESSON 59: "TOMMY SNOOKS"

FEATURED POEM

As Tommy Snooks and Bessy Brooks

Were walking out one Sunday,

Says Tommy Snooks to Bessy Brooks,

"Wilt marry me on Monday?"

SYNOPSIS

Tommy asks Bessy if she will marry him the very next day.

ENRICHMENT ACTIVITIES

1. **Recite Poem Information**
   Practice reciting the title of the poem and the name of the poet.

2. **Narrate the Poem**
   Narrate the poem events or meaning aloud using your own words.

3. **Study the Poem Picture**
   Study the poem picture, and describe how it relates to the poem.

4. **Can You Find It?**
   Find the following in the poem picture: Tommy Snooks, Bessy Brooks, pocket, bonnet, bows, path, and church.

5. **Create Novel Artwork Based on the Poem**
   - One day this week, create artwork of a couple getting married.
   - Use paints, crayons, pastels, Legos, blocks, or Play-Doh to create the artwork.

6. **Explore Rhyming**
   Find and recite the rhyming words in the poem.

VOCABULARY

Students Recite Words	Instructors Read Definitions to Students
Sunday	The first day of the week; it follows Saturday and precedes Monday.
wilt	Archaic term for *will*.
marry	To take a husband or a wife
Monday	The second day of the week; it follows Sunday and precedes Tuesday.

REVIEW QUESTIONS

1. What is the title of the poem?

2. What happens in the poem?

3. What is the setting of the poem?

4. Who are the characters in the poem?

5. Describe the poem picture.

TRACEWORK AND/OR COPYWORK

COLOR THE POEM

LESSON 60: "THE BLACKSMITH"

FEATURED POEM

Robert Barnes, my fellow fine,

Can you shoe this horse of mine?"

"Yes, good sir, that I can,

As well as any other man;

There's a nail, and there's a prod,

Now, good sir, your horse is shod."

SYNOPSIS

The narrator asks a blacksmith to shoe his horse. The blacksmith agrees and does the job.

ENRICHMENT ACTIVITIES

1. **Recite Poem Information**
   Practice reciting the title of the poem and the name of the poet.

2. **Narrate the Poem**
   Narrate the poem events or meaning aloud using your own words.

3. **Study the Poem Picture**
   Study the poem picture, and describe how it relates to the poem.

4. **Can You Find It?**
   Find the following in the poem picture: Robert Barnes, blacksmith, little boy, toy horse, and hammer.

5. **Act Out the Poem**
   As you read the poem, pretend to shoe a horse like a blacksmith.

6. **Create Novel Artwork Based on the Poem**
   - One day this week, create artwork of a horseshoe.
   - Use paints, crayons, pastels, Legos, blocks, or Play-Doh to create the artwork.

7. **Explore Rhyming**
   Find and recite the rhyming words in the poem.

VOCABULARY

Students Recite Words	Instructors Read Definitions to Students
blacksmith	A person who shoes horses; a farrier.
horseshoe	The U-shaped metallic shoe of a horse.
nail	A spike-shaped metal fastener used for joining things together.
prod	A device used to goad livestock into moving.
shod	Wearing shoes.

REVIEW QUESTIONS

1. What is the title of the poem?

2. What happens in the poem?

3. What is the setting of the poem?

4. Who are the characters in the poem?

5. Describe the poem picture.

TRACEWORK AND/OR COPYWORK

COLOR THE POEM

LESSON 61: "COCK-A-DOODLE-DOO"

FEATURED POEM

Cock-a-doodle-doo!

My dame has lost her shoe,

My master's lost his fiddle-stick

And knows not what to do.

Cock-a-doodle-doo!

What is my dame to do?

Till master finds his fiddle-stick,

She'll dance without her shoe.

SYNOPSIS

A fiddler loses his stick and can't play. A lady loses her shoe and cannot dance. The rooster narrator nonsensically claims the lady will dance without her shoe until the fiddler finds his stick.

ENRICHMENT ACTIVITIES

1. **Recite Poem Information**
   Practice reciting the title of the poem and the name of the poet.

2. **Narrate the Poem**
   Narrate the poem events or meaning aloud using your own words.

3. **Study the Poem Picture**
   Study the poem picture, and describe how it relates to the poem.

4. **Can You Find It?**
   Find the following in the poem picture: human foot with no shoe, fiddle with no bow, and rooster.

5. **Act Out the Poem**
   - As you recite the poem, pretend to play a fiddle.
   - Hold the fiddle in one hand while moving the bow back and forth with the other hand.

6. **Create Novel Artwork Based on the Poem**
   - One day this week, create artwork of a fiddle.
   - Use paints, crayons, pastels, Legos, blocks, or Play-Doh to create the artwork.

7. **Explore Rhyming**
   Find and recite the rhyming words in the poem.

VOCABULARY

Students Recite Words	Instructors Read Definitions to Students
dame	A lady, a woman.
master	Someone who has control over something or someone.
fiddle-stick	The bow used to play a fiddle.
fiddle	A stringed instrument played with a bow; a violin.

REVIEW QUESTIONS

1. What is the title of the poem?
2. What happens in the poem?
3. Who are the characters in the poem?
4. Describe the poem picture.

TRACEWORK AND/OR COPYWORK

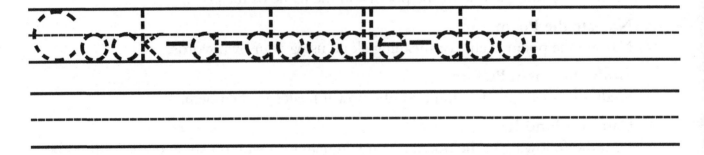

COLOR THE POEM

LESSON 62: "DAPPLE-GRAY"

FEATURED POEM

I had a little pony,

His name was Dapple-Gray,

I lent him to a lady,

To ride a mile away.

She whipped him, she slashed him,

She rode him through the mire;

I would not lend my pony now

For all the lady's hire.

SYNOPSIS

A boy lends his pony to a lady. When the lady mistreats the pony, the boy vows never to lend his pony again.

ENRICHMENT ACTIVITIES

1. **Recite Poem Information**
   Practice reciting the title of the poem and the name of the poet.

2. **Narrate the Poem**
   Narrate the poem events or meaning aloud using your own words.

3. **Study the Poem Picture**
   Study the poem picture, and describe how it relates to the poem.

4. **Can You Find It?**
   Find the following in the poem picture: lady, whip, little boy, horse, bridle, saddle, dapples, hooves, and mane.

5. **Create Novel Artwork Based on the Poem**
   - One day this week, create artwork of something dappled.
   - Use paints, crayons, pastels, Legos, blocks, or Play-Doh to create the artwork.

6. **Explore Rhyming**
   Find and recite the rhyming words in the poem.

VOCABULARY

Students Recite Words	Instructors Read Definitions to Students
pony	Any of several small breeds of horse.
dapple	A mottled marking, usually in clusters.
mile	A customary unit of length.
whipped	Hit or struck.
slashed	Hit with a swift, broad, cutting stroke.
mire	Deep mud; moist, spongy earth.
hire	A group of people who have been hired.

REVIEW QUESTIONS

1. What is the title of the poem?

2. What happens in the poem?

3. Who are the characters in the poem?

4. Does the poem teach us anything?

5. Describe the poem picture.

TRACEWORK AND/OR COPYWORK

COLOR THE POEM

LESSON 63: "COFFEE AND TEA"

FEATURED POEM

Molly, my sister and I fell out,

And what do you think it was all about?

She loved coffee and I loved tea,

And that was the reason we couldn't agree.

SYNOPSIS

Two sisters fight because one likes tea and the other likes coffee.

ENRICHMENT ACTIVITIES

1. **Recite Poem Information**
   Practice reciting the title of the poem and the name of the poet.

2. **Narrate the Poem**
   Narrate the poem events or meaning aloud using your own words.

3. **Study the Poem Picture**
   Study the poem picture, and describe how it relates to the poem.

4. **Can You Find It?**
   Find the following in the poem picture: sisters, cups, saucers, and steam.

5. **Act Out the Poem**
   - Find a partner. Assign one partner to advocate for tea and the other for coffee.
   - Like the sisters in the poem, hold a debate on which is better – tea or coffee?

6. **Create Novel Artwork Based on the Poem**
   - One day this week, create artwork of a cup of coffee or tea.
   - Use paints, crayons, pastels, Legos, blocks, or Play-Doh to create the artwork.

7. **Explore Rhyming**
   Find and recite the rhyming words in the poem.

VOCABULARY

Students Recite Words	Instructors Read Definitions to Students
sister	A daughter of the same parents as another person.
fell out	Had a fight or parting of ways.
coffee	A beverage made by infusing the beans of the coffee plant in hot water.
tea	The drink made by infusing these dried leaves or buds of the tea plant in hot water.
agree	To have the same view or opinion.

REVIEW QUESTIONS

1. What is the title of the poem?

2. What happens in the poem?

3. Who are the characters in the poem?

4. Does the poem teach us anything?

5. Describe the poem picture.

TRACEWORK AND/OR COPYWORK

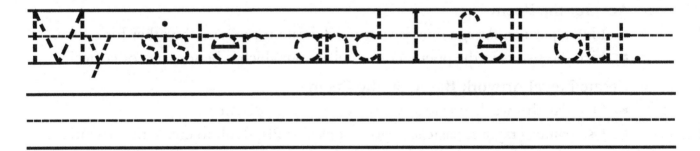

COLOR THE POEM

LESSON 64: "THE LITTLE GIRL WITH A CURL"

FEATURED POEM

There was a little girl who had a little curl

Right in the middle of her forehead;

When she was good, she was very, very good,

And when she was bad she was horrid.

SYNOPSIS

The narrator describes a little girl, who acts in the extreme. She is either very good or plain horrid.

ENRICHMENT ACTIVITIES

1. **Recite Poem Information**
   Practice reciting the title of the poem and the name of the poet.

2. **Narrate the Poem**
   Narrate the poem events or meaning aloud using your own words.

3. **Study the Poem Picture**
   Study the poem picture, and describe how it relates to the poem.

4. **Can You Find It?**
   Find the following in the poem picture: little girl, forehead, curl, dolly, chair, and stripes.

5. **Create Novel Artwork Based on the Poem**
   - One day this week, create artwork of something with a curl or curls.
   - Use paints, crayons, pastels, Legos, blocks, or Play-Doh to create the artwork.

6. **Explore Rhyming**
   Find and recite the rhyming words in the poem.

VOCABULARY

Students Recite Words	Instructors Read Definitions to Students
curl	A piece or lock of curling hair; a ringlet.
horrid	Offensive, disagreeable, or abominable.

REVIEW QUESTIONS

1. What is the title of the poem?

2. What happens in the poem?

3. Who are the characters in the poem?

4. Does the poem teach us anything?

5. Describe the poem picture.

TRACEWORK AND/OR COPYWORK

A little girl with a curl

At times she was horrid

COLOR THE POEM

LESSON 65: "CANDLE-SAVING"

FEATURED POEM

To make your candles last for aye,

You wives and maids give ear-O!

To put them out's the only way,

Says honest John Boldero.

SYNOPSIS

Honest John advises all that the only way to save candles
is to put them out.

ENRICHMENT ACTIVITIES

1. **Recite Poem Information**
   Practice reciting the title of the poem and the name of the poet.

2. **Narrate the Poem**
   Narrate the poem events or meaning aloud using your own words.

3. **Study the Poem Picture**
   Study the poem picture, and describe how it relates to the poem.

4. **Can You Find It?**
   Find the following in the poem picture: John Boldero, raised finger, candle, flame,
   candlestick, rope belt, and slippers.

5. **Create Novel Artwork Based on the Poem**
   - One day this week, sculpt a lit candle. Sculpt the wax, the wick, and the flame.
   - Use Play-Doh to create the artwork.

6. **Explore Rhyming**
   Find and recite the rhyming words in the poem.

VOCABULARY

Students Recite Words	Instructors Read Definitions to Students
aye	Archaic term for *always*.
maids	Girls or unmarried young women.
honest	Someone who tells the truth.

REVIEW QUESTIONS

1. What is the title of the poem?

2. What happens in the poem?

3. Who are the characters in the poem?

4. Does the poem teach us anything?

5. Describe the poem picture.

TRACEWORK AND/OR COPYWORK

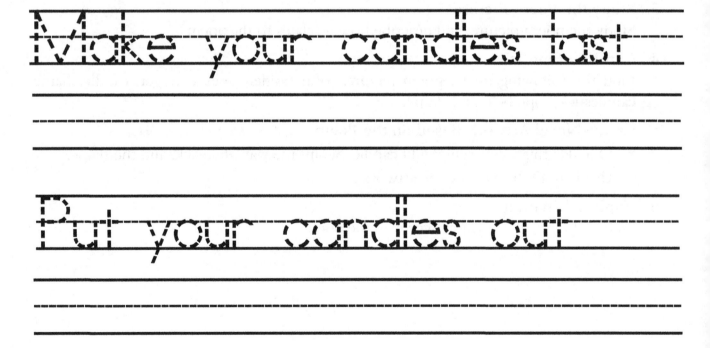

COLOR THE POEM

LESSON 66: "LADYBIRD"

FEATURED POEM

Ladybird, ladybird, fly away home!

Your house is on fire, your children all gone,

All but one, and her name is Ann,

And she crept under the pudding pan.

SYNOPSIS

The narrator tries to convince a ladybug to fly away by telling tall tales.

ENRICHMENT ACTIVITIES

1. **Recite Poem Information**
   Practice reciting the title of the poem and the name of the poet.

2. **Narrate the Poem**
   Narrate the poem events or meaning aloud using your own words.

3. **Study the Poem Picture**
   Study the poem picture, and describe how it relates to the poem.

4. **Can You Find It?**
   Find the following in the poem picture: girl, boy, path, ladybug, tree, and town.

5. **Create Novel Artwork Based on the Poem**
   - One day this week, create artwork of a ladybug's house on fire.
   - Use paints, crayons, pastels, Legos, blocks, or Play-Doh to create the artwork.

6. **Explore Rhyming**
   Find and recite the rhyming words in the poem.

VOCABULARY

Students Recite Words	Instructors Read Definitions to Students
ladybird	Another term for *ladybug*.
crept	To move slowly with the abdomen close to the ground.
pudding	Any of various dishes, sweet or savory, prepared by boiling or steaming, or from batter.

REVIEW QUESTIONS

1. What is the title of the poem?

2. What happens in the poem?

3. What is the setting of the poem?

4. Who are the characters in the poem?

5. Describe the poem picture.

TRACEWORK AND/OR COPYWORK

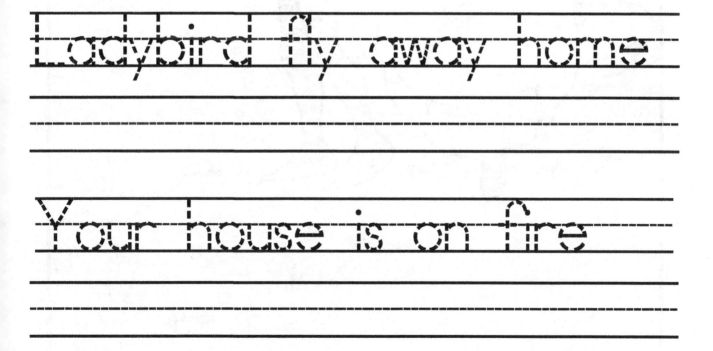

COLOR THE POEM

LESSON 67: "CAESAR'S SONG"

FEATURED POEM

Bow-wow-wow!

Whose dog art thou?

Little Tom Tinker's dog,

Bow-wow-wow!

SYNOPSIS

The narrator asks a dog about his owner. The dog tells the narrator he belongs to Tom Tinker.

ENRICHMENT ACTIVITIES

1. **Recite Poem Information**
   Practice reciting the title of the poem and the name of the poet.

2. **Narrate the Poem**
   Narrate the poem events or meaning aloud using your own words.

3. **Study the Poem Picture**
   Study the poem picture, and describe how it relates to the poem.

4. **Can You Find It?**
   Find the following in the poem picture: Tom Tinker, dog, leash, dog house, dog dish, collar, bone, creeping vine, and wall.

5. **Create Novel Artwork Based on the Poem**
   - One day this week, create artwork of a dog house.
   - Use paints, crayons, pastels, Legos, blocks, or Play-Doh to create the artwork.

6. **Explore Rhyming**
   Find and recite the rhyming words in the poem.

VOCABULARY

Students Recite Words	Instructors Read Definitions to Students
Caesar	An ancient Roman family name, notably that of Julius Caesar.
art	Archaic term for *are*.
thou	Archaic term for *you*.
tinker	1. A person who makes and mends household utensils made of tin. 2. To fiddle with something in an attempt to fix, mend or improve it, especially in an experimental or unskilled manner.

REVIEW QUESTIONS

1. What is the title of the poem?

2. Why do you think the title of the poem is "Caesar's Song?"

3. What happens in the poem?

4. Who are the characters in the poem?

5. Describe the poem picture.

TRACEWORK AND/OR COPYWORK

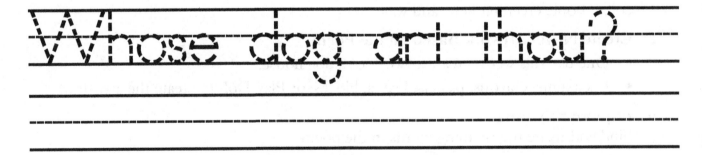

COLOR THE POEM

LESSON 68: "AS I WAS GOING ALONG"

FEATURED POEM

As I was going along, along,

A-singing a comical song, song, song,

The lane that I went was so long, long, long,

And the song that I sang was so long, long, long,

And so I went singing along.

SYNOPSIS

The narrator sings and walks down a long lane.

ENRICHMENT ACTIVITIES

1. **Recite Poem Information**
   Practice reciting the title of the poem and the name of the poet.

2. **Narrate the Poem**
   Narrate the poem events or meaning aloud using your own words.

3. **Study the Poem Picture**
   Study the poem picture, and describe how it relates to the poem.

4. **Can You Find It?**
   Find the following in the poem picture: someone singing, cap, lane, house, and hands in pockets.

5. **Act Out the Poem**
   - Pretend your hand is the poem narrator
   - As you recite the poem, open and close your fingers to mimic singing and walk your hand across your desk or table.

6. **Explore Rhyming**
   Find and recite the rhyming words in the poem.

VOCABULARY

Students Recite Words	Instructors Read Definitions to Students
comical	Funny, whimsically amusing.
lane	A road, street, or other path.
long	1. Having much distance. 2. Lasting an extended amount of time.

REVIEW QUESTIONS

1. What is the title of the poem?

2. What happens in the poem?

3. What is the setting of the poem?

4. Who are the characters in the poem?

5. Describe the poem picture.

TRACEWORK AND/OR COPYWORK

COLOR THE POEM

LESSON 69: "LITTLE JACK HORNER"

FEATURED POEM

Little Jack Horner

Sat in the corner,

Eating of Christmas pie:

He put in his thumb,

And pulled out a plum,

And said, "What a good boy am I!"

SYNOPSIS

Jack puts his thumb in a pie, pulls out a plumb, and says he is a good boy.

ENRICHMENT ACTIVITIES

1. **Recite Poem Information**
   Practice reciting the title of the poem and the name of the poet.

2. **Narrate the Poem**
   Narrate the poem events or meaning aloud using your own words.

3. **Study the Poem Picture**
   Study the poem picture, and describe how it relates to the poem.

4. **Can You Find It?**
   Find the following in the poem picture: little boy, cat, bow, Christmas pie, corner, and stool.

5. **Act Out the Poem**
   As you recite the poem, pretend to stick your thumb in a pie, pull a plum out, and pretend to eat the plum.

6. **Create Novel Artwork Based on the Poem**
   - One day this week, create a sculpture of a pie out of Play-Doh or modeling clay.
   - Build the base crust, the filling (make lots of round plums), and the top crust.
   - Pretend to be Jack. Stick your thumb in your pie and fish out a plum.

7. **Explore Rhyming**
   Find and recite the rhyming words in the poem.

VOCABULARY

Students Recite Words	Instructors Read Definitions to Students
corner	The place where two walls meet.
Christmas pie	A pie made especially for the Christmas holiday time.
plum	An edible, fleshy stone fruit, often of a dark red or purple color.

REVIEW QUESTIONS

1. What is the title of the poem?

2. What happens in the poem?

3. What is the setting of the poem?

4. Who are the characters in the poem?

5. Describe the poem picture.

TRACEWORK AND/OR COPYWORK

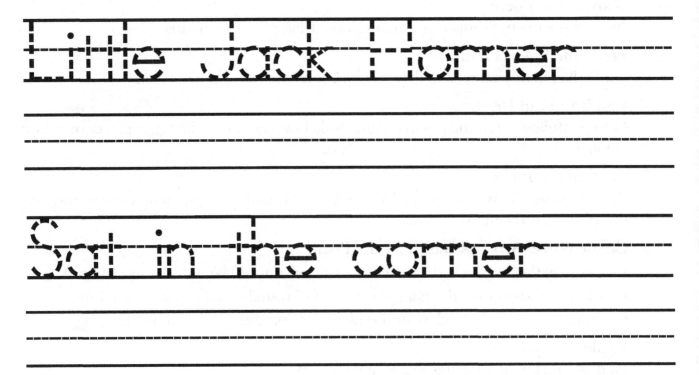

COLOR THE POEM

LESSON 70: "MARY, MARY, QUITE CONTRARY"

FEATURED POEM

Mary, Mary, quite contrary,

How does your garden grow?

With silver bells and cockle-shells,

And pretty maids all in a row.

SYNOPSIS

The narrator asks Mary about her garden. Mary describes her garden. There are silver bells, cockle shells, and pretty maids lined up in a row.

ENRICHMENT ACTIVITIES

1. **Recite Poem Information**
   Practice reciting the title of the poem and the name of the poet.

2. **Narrate the Poem**
   Narrate the poem events or meaning aloud using your own words.

3. **Study the Poem Picture**
   Study the poem picture, and describe how it relates to the poem.

4. **Can You Find It?**
   Find the following in the poem picture: Mary, rake, flower hat, cockle-shells, watering can, pretty maids, and silver bells.

5. **Create Novel Artwork Based on the Poem**
   - One day this week, create artwork of a garden of beautiful flowers.
   - Use paints, crayons, pastels, Legos, blocks, or Play-Doh to create the artwork.

6. **Explore Rhyming**
   Find and recite the rhyming words in the poem.

VOCABULARY

Students Recite Words	Instructors Read Definitions to Students
contrary	Opposite; in an opposite direction; given to opposition.
cockle-shells (cockleshells)	The shell of a cockle, a mollusk with two hinged heart-shaped shells.
row	A line of objects.

REVIEW QUESTIONS

1. What is the title of the poem?

2. What happens in the poem.

3. Who are the characters in the poem?

4. Describe the poem picture.

TRACEWORK AND/OR COPYWORK

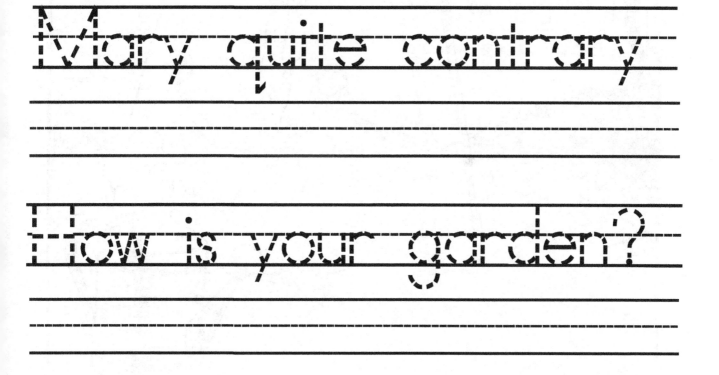

COLOR THE POEM

LESSON 71: "MARY'S CANARY"

FEATURED POEM

Mary had a pretty bird,
Feathers bright and yellow,
Slender legs--upon my word
He was a pretty fellow!

The sweetest note he always sung,
Which much delighted Mary.
She often, where the cage was hung,
Sat hearing her canary.

SYNOPSIS

Mary has a pretty canary in a cage. She enjoys listening to the bird sing.

ENRICHMENT ACTIVITIES

1. **Recite Poem Information**
   Practice reciting the title of the poem and the name of the poet.

2. **Narrate the Poem**
   Narrate the poem events or meaning aloud using your own words.

3. **Study the Poem Picture**
   Study the poem picture, and describe how it relates to the poem.

4. **Can You Find It?**
   Find the following in the poem picture: Mary, canary, bird cage, bench, and rug.

5. **Create Novel Artwork Based on the Poem**
   - One day this week, paint or draw a bird singing in a cage.
   - Use paints, crayons, or pastels to create the artwork.

6. **Explore Rhyming**
   Find and recite the rhyming words in the poem.

VOCABULARY

Students Recite Words	Instructors Read Definitions to Students
slender	Thin; slim.
fellow	A male companion.
note	A musical sound.
cage	An enclosure made of bars, normally to hold animals.
canary	A small songbird, usually yellow.

REVIEW QUESTIONS

1. What is the title of the poem?

2. What happens in the poem?

3. Who are the characters in the poem?

4. Describe the poem picture.

TRACEWORK AND/OR COPYWORK

COLOR THE POEM

LESSON 72: "THE LITTLE BIRD"

FEATURED POEM

Once I saw a little bird

Come hop, hop, hop;

So I cried, "Little bird,

Will you stop, stop, stop?"

And was going to the window

To say, "How do you do?"

But he shook his little tail,

And far away he flew.

SYNOPSIS

The narrator sees a little bird and asks it to stay, but it flies away.

ENRICHMENT ACTIVITIES

1. **Recite Poem Information**
   Practice reciting the title of the poem and the name of the poet.

2. **Narrate the Poem**
   Narrate the poem events or meaning aloud using your own words.

3. **Study the Poem Picture**
   Study the poem picture, and describe how it relates to the poem.

4. **Can You Find It?**
   Find the following in the poem picture: little boy, wind-blown hair, curtains, curtain rod, and window.

5. **Act Out the Poem**
   - As you recite the poem, enact the roles of the boy and the bird with your hands.
   - One hand plays the boy asking the bird to stay.
   - The other hand plays the bird hopping, flapping their wings, and flying away.

6. **Explore Rhyming**
   Find and recite the rhyming words in the poem.

VOCABULARY

Students Recite Words	Instructors Read Definitions to Students
hop	A short jump.
shook	Moved rapidly in alternating directions.

oooo09

1. What is the title of the poem?

2. What happens in the poem?

3. What is the setting of the poem?

4. Who are the characters in the poem?

5. Describe the poem picture.

TRACEWORK AND/OR COPYWORK

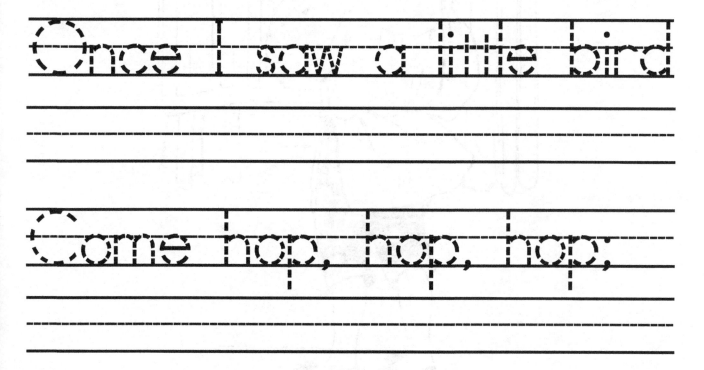

COLOR THE POEM

ANSWERS TO REVIEW QUESTIONS

LESSON 1

1. **What is the title of the poem?** The poem title is "Rain."
2. **What happens in the poem?** The narrator asks the rain to stop so Johnny can go outside.
3. **What is the setting of the poem?** The poem takes place inside on a rainy day or perhaps outside under an umbrella or other shelter.
4. **Who are the characters in the poem?** The characters are the narrator and Johnny.
5. **Does the poem teach us anything?** The poem reminds us that bad weather may spoil our outdoor plans.
6. **Describe the poem picture.** The picture shows a little boy under an umbrella outside in the rain. He has a toy horse on wheels. A duck quacks at him from a stream. He looks up at the clouds. As expressed by the narrator in the poem, the boy is probably wishing the rain would stop.

LESSON 2

1. **What is the title of the poem?** The poem title is "The Clock."
2. **What happens in the poem?** A clock with two hands points out the time.
3. **What is the setting of the poem?** The poem takes place in a schoolroom.
4. **Who are the characters in the poem?** The characters are the narrator and perhaps children in a schoolroom.
5. **Does the poem teach us anything?** The poem tells us children should be clean and helpful, like the clock.
6. **Describe the poem picture.** The picture shows a little girl looking up at a clock's bright face and two hands. The clock tells the girl the time.

LESSON 3

1. **What is the title of the poem?** The poem title is "Fingers and Toes."
2. **What happens in the poem?** This poem is a riddle that appears to make outlandish claims. Upon closer study, the poem only makes true statements.
3. **Who are the characters in the poem?** The characters are the narrator and every lady in the land.
4. **Does the poem teach us anything?** The poem teaches us that punctuation and spacing are important.
5. **What is the answer to the poem riddle?** Considering proper punctuation, the poem makes the following true statements. Every lady in this land has twenty nails. Every lady has five nails upon each hand. Every lady has twenty nails on hands and feet.

LESSON 4

1. **What is the title of the poem?** The poem title is "The Old Woman Under a Hill."
2. **What happens in the poem?** An old woman lives under a hill.
3. **Who are the characters in the poem?** The characters are the narrator and the old woman.
4. **Does the poem teach us anything?** The poem contains a statement that logically must always be true – "And if she's not gone, She lives there still." She's either there or not there.
5. **Describe the poem picture.** As described in the poem, the picture shows the old woman sitting on a bench outside her home in the hill. She is busy making or mending a sock.

LESSON 5

1. **What is the title of the poem?** The poem title is "Oh, Dear!"
2. **What happens in the poem?** Two old women climb an apple tree and come down at different times.
3. **What is the setting of the poem?** The poem takes place outside in an apple tree.
4. **Who are the characters in the poem?** The characters are the narrator and two old women.
5. **Describe the poem picture.** As described in the poem, the picture shows an old woman wearing a dress and a hat sitting up in an apple tree.

LESSON 6

1. **What is the title of the poem?** The poem title is "Pat-A-Cake."
2. **What happens in the poem?** The narrator asks the baker's man to make a cake for Tommy and themselves.
3. **What is the setting of the poem?** The poem takes place in a bakery.
4. **Who are the characters in the poem?** The characters are the baker's man, Tommy, and the narrator.
5. **Describe the poem picture.** As described in the poem, the picture shows two small children watching a baker holding a freshly baked pie.

LESSON 7

1. **What is the title of the poem?** The poem title is "Jack."
2. **What happens in the poem?** A person named Jack jumps over a candlestick.
3. **Who are the characters in the poem?** The characters in the poem are the narrator and Jack.
4. **Does the poem teach us anything?** You must be nimble and quick to successfully jump over a candlestick.
5. **Describe the poem picture.** As described in the poem, the picture shows Jack in pajamas and a nightcap jumping over a candlestick. The candlestick holds a lit candle.

LESSON 8

1. **What is the title of the poem?** The poem title is "Baby Dolly."
2. **What happens in the poem?** A little girl pretends her baby doll is fussing and offers food to the doll if the doll won't cry.
3. **Who are the characters in the poem?** The characters are a little girl and her dolly.
4. **Describe the poem picture.** As described in the poem, the picture shows a little girl and her dolly sitting on a rug. The little girl raises a finger as she hushes her doll.

LESSON 9

1. **What is the title of the poem?** The poem title is "Bees."
2. **What happens in the poem?** The poem captures when bees are most valuable for pollinating crops.
3. **Does the poem teach us anything?** That bees are valuable for crop pollination in May, even more valuable for crop pollination in June, but by the time July comes, bees can no longer help to grow crops.
4. **Describe the poem picture.** The picture shows a child looking at an active beehive up in a tree.

LESSON 10

1. **What is the title of the poem?** The poem title is "If Wishes Were Horses."
2. **What happens in the poem?** The poem compares the value and availability of things.
3. **Who are the characters in the poem?** The characters are beggars, tinkers, and the narrator.
4. **Does the poem teach us anything?** The poem teaches that scarce items tend to cost more than widely available items.
5. **Describe the poem picture.** The picture illustrates the first line of the poem, showing a beggar riding a white horse at an intersection.

LESSON 11

1. **What is the title of the poem?** The poem title is "To Market."
2. **What happens in the poem?** The narrator goes to market, buys a pig and a bun, and brings the pig home.
3. **What is the setting of the poem?** The poem takes place at the narrator's home, on the path to and from the market, and at the market.
4. **Who are the characters in the poem?** The character is the narrator who buys the pig and bun.
5. **Describe the poem picture.** The picture shows two children leading a pig down a path. The boy holds a string tied to the pig's hind foot.

LESSON 12

1. **What is the title of the poem?** The poem title is "Lucy Locket."
2. **What happens in the poem?** Lucy Locket lost her pocket. It is returned to her empty.
3. **Who are the characters in the poem?** The characters are the narrator, Lucy Locket, and Kitty Fisher.
4. **Does the poem teach us anything?** Be careful with your belongings. If you lose them, they may not be returned to you in the same condition as when you lost them.
5. **Describe the poem picture.** The picture illustrates the first two lines of the poem. Lucy Locket walks in the snow and cries into her hankie. Kitty Fisher runs toward Lucy, the pocket clutched high in Kitty's grasp.

LESSON 13

1. **What is the title of the poem?** The poem title is "Two Birds."
2. **What happens in the poem?** Two birds sit on a stone. One by one they fly away.
3. **What is the setting of the poem?** The poem takes place outside on a stone.
4. **Does the poem teach us anything?** The poem provides a subtraction word problem, where 2-1 is 1 and 1-1 is none.
5. **Describe the poem picture.** The picture illustrates the third line of the poem. One bird sits on a stone, and the other has flown away.

LESSON 14

1. **What is the title of the poem?** The poem title is "The Flying Pig."
2. **What happens in the poem?** A pig flies into the air. A man brings him back down.
3. **Who are the characters in the poem?** The characters are the narrator, the man in brown, and the pig.
4. **Does the poem teach us anything?** We know pigs don't fly, so how can this rhyme be true? The picture shows one explanation for how the rhyme could be true.
5. **Describe the poem picture.** The picture shows a man flying a kite decorated with a pig. Two children look on with delight.

LESSON 15

1. **What is the title of the poem?** The poem title is "Hush-a-bye."
2. **What happens in the poem?** A baby in a cradle rocks in a tree and falls.
3. **What is the setting of the poem?** The poem takes place in and around a tree.
4. **Who are the characters in the poem?** The characters are the narrator and the baby.
5. **Describe the poem picture.** The picture shows a baby in a cradle. The cradle is tied to a tree bough.

LESSON 16

1. **What is the title of the poem?** The poem title is "The Three Wise Men of Gotham."
2. **What happens in the poem?** Three men set out to sea in a bowl. They never come back.
3. **What is the setting of the poem?** The poem takes place at sea.
4. **Who are the characters in the poem?** The characters are the narrator and the three men.
5. **Were the wise men of Gotham in the poem actually wise?** No, the men were not wise. The sea can be wild and dangerous, and sailing the sea in a bowl is quite foolish.
6. **Does the poem teach us anything?** The poem advises us to use common sense. We don't know why the men never came back, but it is likely the men perished at sea, since a bowl would not be very seaworthy.
7. **Describe the poem picture.** The picture shows three men riding in a bowl in the sea. Seagulls fly around them. One man peers through a looking glass.

LESSON 17

1. **What is the title of the poem?** The poem title is "Pussy-cat and Queen."
2. **What happens in the poem?** A cat travels to London to see the Queen. While there, the cat scares a mouse under a chair.
3. **What is the setting of the poem?** The poem takes place wherever the cat lives and references London.
4. **Who are the characters in the poem?** The characters are the narrator, the cat, the mouse, and the Queen.
5. **Describe the poem picture.** In the picture, a young lady and a cat meet on a path.

LESSON 18

1. **What is the title of the poem?** The poem title is "Christmas."
2. **What happens in the poem?** The poem points out that Christmas is rare, but lots of fun.
3. **Describe the poem picture.** The picture shows a Christmas tree, which is decorated once a year for Christmas.

LESSON 19

1. **What is the title of the poem?** The poem title is "ABC."
2. **Does the poem teach us anything?** The poem introduces the letters A, B, and C.
3. **Who are the characters in the poem?** The characters are the narrator, the little girl, and the hiding cat.
4. **Describe the poem picture.** The poem picture shows a little girl about to peek into a cupboard. Letter blocks are scattered on the floor.

LESSON 20

1. **What is the title of the poem?** The poem title is "Banbury Cross."
2. **What happens in the poem?** A lady rides through Banbury Cross with bells on her toes, making music.
3. **What is the setting of the poem?** The poem takes place at a crossroad in Banbury, England
4. **Who are the characters in the poem?** The characters are the child narrator and the lady.
5. **Describe the poem picture.** The picture shows a lady riding a white horse. She has rings on her fingers and bells on her toes. The townsfolk stop to watch her ride.

LESSON 21

1. **What is the title of the poem?** The poem title is "Wee Willie Winkie."
2. **What happens in the poem?** Willie runs through the town, making sure the children are in bed.
3. **What is the setting of the poem?** The poem takes place in a town.
4. **Who are the characters in the poem?** The characters are the narrator, the Willie, and the townsfolk.
5. **Does the poem teach us anything?** It is important for children to go to bed early and get their sleep.
6. **Describe the poem picture.** Willie Winkie stands on a bench on tiptoe. He peers into a window to see if the children are in bed.

LESSON 22

1. **What is the title of the poem?** The poem title is "See-saw."
2. **What happens in the poem?** This poem contains a rhyme for children to say as they ride up and down on a seesaw.
3. **Who are the characters in the poem?** The main characters are the narrator and Margery Daw.
4. **Describe the poem picture.** The picture shows a boy and a girl riding a seesaw. A beehive buzzes with bees in the distance.

LESSON 23

1. **What is the title of the poem?** The poem title is "Five Toes."
2. **What happens in the poem?** The poem refers to each of the five toes on a little foot.
3. **Who are the characters in the poem?** The characters are the narrator and the owner of the five little piggies (toes).
4. **Describe the poem picture.** The picture shows a woman touching a child's toe.

LESSON 24

1. **What is the title of the poem?** The poem title is "Three Blind Mice."
2. **What happens in the poem?** The three blind mice chase a farmer's wife.
3. **Who are the characters in the poem?** The characters are the narrator, the three mice, and the farmer's wife.
4. **Describe the poem picture.** Three mice chase a woman through a kitchen.

LESSON 25

1. **What is the title of the poem?** The poem title is "Diddle Diddle Dumpling."
2. **What happens in the poem?** John falls asleep with his breeches and one sock still on.
3. **What is the setting of the poem?** The poem takes place in John's bedroom.
4. **Who are the characters in the poem?** The narrator (John's father) and his son, John.
5. **Describe the poem picture.** The poem picture shows a little boy asleep on the bed wearing his shirt, short pants (breeches), and one sock.

LESSON 26

1. **What is the title of the poem?** The poem title is "The Black Hen."
2. **What happens in the poem?** A black hen lays eggs for gentlemen.
3. **What is the setting of the poem?** The poem takes place at a farm/henhouse.
4. **Who are the characters in the poem?** The characters include the narrator who owns the hen, the hen, and the gentlemen.
5. **Describe the poem picture.** In the picture, two gentlemen watch the black hen.

LESSON 27

1. **What is the title of the poem?** The poem title is "A Candle."
2. **What happens in the poem?** The poem is a riddle. Nanny Etticoat is a candle (white petticoat) with a red flame (nose). The candle grows shorter the longer it burns.
3. **Who are the characters in the poem?** The characters are the narrator and Nanny Etticoat, the candle.
4. **Describe the poem picture.** The picture shows a burning white candle with a face.

LESSON 28

1. **What is the title of the poem?** The poem title is "Curly-locks."
2. **What happens in the poem?** The narrator asks Curly-locks to be his and promises a leisurely life of sitting on cushions, sewing, and eating strawberries and cream. Curly-locks will not even have to do the dishes.
3. **Who are the characters in the poem?** The characters are the narrator and Curly-locks.
4. **Describe the poem picture.** In the picture, Curly-locks lives the life that the poem narrator imagines for her. She sits and sews, eats strawberries and cream, and has a pet bird.

LESSON 29
1. **What is the title of the poem?** The poem title is "Humpty Dumpty."
2. **What happens in the poem?** Humpty Dumpty, the egg, falls, breaks, and can't be fixed.
3. **What is the setting of the poem?** The poem takes place on a high wall.
4. **Who are the characters in the poem?** The characters are the narrator, Humpty Dumpty, and the king's men.
5. **Does the poem teach us anything?** The poem points out that some things, once broken, can't be fixed.
6. **Describe the poem picture.** In the picture, Humpty Dumpty has lost his balance and topples off the wall.

LESSON 30
1. **What is the title of the poem?** The poem title is "Pins."
2. **What happens in the poem?** The poem provides the reader advice.
3. **Does the poem teach us anything?** The poem teaches us to waste not, want not.
4. **Describe the poem picture.** The poem picture shows a mother bending down after sweeping, pointing at a pin to pick up. Her young daughter looks on.

LESSON 31
1. **What is the title of the poem?** The poem title is "The Mouse and the Clock."
2. **What happens in the poem?** A mouse runs up a clock. When the clock gongs one o'clock, the mouse runs back down.
3. **What is the setting of the poem?** The poem takes place in a house with a clock.
4. **Who are the characters in the poem?** The characters are the narrator and a mouse.
5. **Does the poem teach us anything?** The poem teaches us that loud noises may startle animals (and humans too).
6. **Describe the poem picture.** The poem picture shows a mouse leaping off the side of a clock. The clock's hands point to one o'clock.

LESSON 32
1. **What is the title of the poem?** The poem title is "Jack Jelf."
2. **What happens in the poem?** A boy is placed on a shelf due to his difficulties with spelling. He cannot spell "pie." The narrator does not help Jack, but leaves him there to sit on the shelf.
3. **What is the setting of the poem?** The poem takes place inside a building or a home.
4. **Who are the characters in the poem?** The characters are the narrator, Jack Jelf, and Jack's aunt, Mrs. Grace.
5. **Describe the poem picture.** The picture shows a small boy sitting on a wooden shelf. His feet dangle down.

LESSON 33
1. **What is the title of the poem?** The poem title is "Jack Sprat."
2. **What happens in the poem?** The poem remarks on the compatibility of a husband and wife. One eats fat, the other lean, and together they cooperate to eat everything.
3. **What is the setting of the poem?** The poem takes place at the dinner table.
4. **Who are the characters in the poem?** The characters are the narrator, Jack Sprat, and his wife.
5. **Does the poem teach us anything?** The poem implies that cooperation and sharing are beneficial things - often everyone wins (except for perhaps the hungry cat shown in the poem picture.)
6. **Describe the poem picture.** The picture shows Jack and his wife at the dinner table eating. The wife offers Jack something fatty, and Jack declines. A cat sits on the floor and looks up at the food longingly.

LESSON 34

1. **What is the title of the poem?** The poem title is "Hush-a-bye."
2. **What happens in the poem?** A daddy takes care of a baby. He talks or sings the poem to calm the baby.
3. **What is the setting of the poem?** The poem takes place at the family's home.
4. **Who are the characters in the poem?** The characters are the daddy (the narrator), the mommy, and the baby.
5. **Describe the poem picture.** The picture shows a man trying to calm a crying baby in a cradle.

LESSON 35

1. **What is the title of the poem?** The poem title is "Nancy Dawson."
2. **What happens in the poem?** Nancy Dawson lies in bed and does not work.
3. **Who are the characters in the poem?** The characters are the narrator, the narrator's "honey," and Nancy Dawson.
4. **Does the poem teach us anything?** The narrator of the poem provides an example of someone being little gossipy and nosy.
5. **Describe the poem picture.** The picture shows Nancy Dawson tucked in bed sleeping. The sun's light shines yellow through the window, showing it is daytime.

LESSON 36

1. **What is the title of the poem?** The poem title is "The Alphabet."
2. **What happens in the poem?** The poem is to be read or recited aloud for learning the alphabet.
3. **Does the poem teach us anything?** The poem helps the reciter to learn their ABCs.
4. **Describe the poem picture.** The poem picture shows a girl playing with alphabet blocks.

LESSON 37

1. **What is the title of the poem?** The poem title is "Jack and Jill."
2. **What happens in the poem?** Jack and Jill fall down a hill while trying to get water from a well. Jack runs to Dame Dob to fix his hurt head.
3. **What is the setting of the poem?** The poem takes place outside on a hill.
4. **Who are the characters in the poem?** The characters are the narrator, Jack, Jill, and Dame Dob.
5. **Does the poem teach us anything?** The poem teaches us to watch where we walk and be careful not to trip.
6. **Describe the poem picture.** The poem picture shows that Jack and Jill have almost reached the well at the top of the hill. Jack holds a bucket for the water. It is just before they fall and tumble down the hill.

LESSON 38

1. **What is the title of the poem?** The poem title is "Dance to Your Daddy."
2. **What happens in the poem?** The narrator tells a little boy to dance upon his father return from a fishing trip.
3. **Who are the characters in the poem?** The characters are the narrator, the laddie, and the laddie's daddie.
4. **How do we know the poem refers to a son and not a daughter?** "Laddie" refers to a young boy.
5. **Describe the poem picture.** The poem picture shows a woman helping a toddler walk.

LESSON 39
1. **What is the title of the poem?** The poem title is "One Misty Moisty Morning."
2. **What happens in the poem?** A girl meets an old man. He compliments her and she smiles.
3. **What is the setting of the poem?** The poem takes place outside on a misty day.
4. **Who are the characters in the poem?** The characters are the narrator and an old man.
5. **Does the poem teach us anything?** The poem provides an example of two people greeting each other politely.
6. **Describe the poem picture.** The poem picture shows a girl under an umbrella speaking with an old man holding a cane.

LESSON 40
1. **What is the title of the poem?** The poem title is "The Old Woman from France."
2. **What happens in the poem?** An old woman tries to teach children to dance. When the children are too stiff, she sends them home.
3. **What is the setting of the poem?** The poem takes place in a room where dance lessons are taught.
4. **Who are the characters in the poem?** The characters are the narrator, a dance teacher, and dance students.
5. **Describe the poem picture.** The picture shows a lady teaching a girl and a boy to dance.

LESSON 41
1. **What is the title of the poem?** The poem title is "My Kitten."
2. **What happens in the poem?** The narrator says an ode to their kitten.
3. **Who are the characters in the poem?** The characters are the narrator and the kitten.
4. **Describe the poem picture.** The poem picture shows an old woman sitting in a chair and working on a sock. A kitten plays nearby with a ball of yarn.

LESSON 42
1. **What is the title of the poem?** The poem title is "Pancake Day."
2. **What happens in the poem?** The poem addresses, pancake day, a day in Great Britain before Lent, where people make pancakes to use up eggs and milk. There poem also mentions ball throwing.
3. **Describe the poem picture.** The poem picture shows two children playing catch with a dog running nearby.

LESSON 43
1. **What is the title of the poem?** The poem title is "The Merchants of London."
2. **What happens in the poem?** The poem discusses the fancy dress of the merchants of London.
3. **Who are the characters in the poem?** The characters are the narrator and the merchants of London.
4. **Describe the poem picture.** The poem picture shows the merchants of London dressed in fancy, bright clothing.

LESSON 44
1. **What is the title of the poem?** The poem title is "Sleep Baby Sleep."
2. **What happens in the poem?** The poem is a lullaby. The narrator sings a baby to sleep.
3. **What is the setting of the poem?** The poem most likely takes place in a baby's bedroom.
4. **Who are the characters in the poem?** The characters are the narrator and the baby.
5. **Describe the poem picture.** The poem picture shows a woman leaning over a baby's cradle, trying to soothe the baby to sleep.

LESSON 45

1. **What is the title of the poem?** The poem title is "Baa Baa Black Sheep."
2. **What happens in the poem?** The narrator asks if there is wool, and the sheep answers there is wool for his master and his dame.
3. **Who are the characters in the poem?** The characters are the sheep, the master, the dame, the little boy, and the narrator.
4. **Does the poem teach us anything?** The poems teaches us that we may miss out on things if we fuss and cry.
5. **Describe the poem picture.** The poem picture shows a little girl and boy looking at a black sheep on a path.

LESSON 46

1. **What is the title of the poem?** The poem title is "The Cat and the Fiddle."
2. **What happens in the poem?** In the poem, the cat has a fiddle, the cow jumps over the moon, the dog laughs, and the dish and spoon run away.
3. **Who are the characters in the poem?** The characters are the narrator, the cat, the cow, the dog, the dish, and the spoon.
4. **Describe the poem picture.** The poem picture shows a cat playing a fiddle, a laughing dog in a clown outfit, a cow jumping over a moon, and a dish and a spoon running and holding hands.

LESSON 47

1. **What is the title of the poem?** The poem title is "Sing a Song of Sixpence."
2. **What happens in the poem?** The king is served a pie of live blackbirds and counts his money, the queen eats bread and honey in the parlor, and a black bird bites the maid on the nose.
3. **What is the setting of the poem?** The poem takes place at the king and queen's palace.
4. **Who are the characters in the poem?** The characters are the narrator, the king, the queen, and the maid.
5. **Describe the poem picture.** The poem picture shows the king cutting open his pie and the blackbirds emerging and singing.

LESSON 48

1. **What is the title of the poem?** The poem title is "Tommy Tittlemouse."
2. **What happens in the poem?** Tommy lives in a small house and catches fish on land owned by others.
3. **Who are the characters in the poem?** The characters are the narrator, Tommy, and those that own the land on which he fishes.
4. **Describe the poem picture.** The poem picture shows Tommy trespassing by fishing on someone else's land.

LESSON 49

1. **What is the title of the poem?** The poem title is "The Hobby-Horse."
2. **What happens in the poem?** The narrator sells their toy horse to an old woman and later regrets it.
3. **Who are the characters in the poem?** The characters are the narrator and the woman who bought the toy horse.
4. **Describe the poem picture.** The poem picture shows a boy with a toy horse talking to a woman.

LESSON 50

1. **What is the title of the poem?** The poem title is "Boy and the Sparrow."
2. **What happens in the poem?** A boy wants to shoot a sparrow to make stew and pie. The sparrow escapes.
3. **What is the setting of the poem?** The poem takes place outside, near a tree.
4. **Who are the characters in the poem?** The characters are the narrator, the boy, and the sparrow.
5. **Describe the poem picture.** The poem picture shows a boy holding a bow and arrows and watching a sparrow in a tree.

LESSON 51

1. **What is the title of the poem?** The poem title is "Old Woman, Old Woman."
2. **What happens in the poem?** A woman in a basket travels higher than the moon to sweep the cobwebs from the sky.
3. **What is the setting of the poem?** The poem takes place in the sky.
4. **Who are the characters in the poem?** The characters are the narrator and the old woman.
5. **Describe the poem picture.** The poem shows an old woman in a basket, higher than the moon. She holds a broom.

LESSON 52

1. **What is the title of the poem?** The poem title is "Two Pigeons."
2. **What happens in the poem?** Two of the narrator's pigeons fly away for an unknown reason.
3. **Who are the characters in the poem?** The characters are the narrator and the pigeons.
4. **Describe the poem picture.** The poem picture shows a girl holding a dish and looking at a bird house. Birds swoop around the bird house.

LESSON 53

1. **What is the title of the poem?** The poem title is "The First of May."
2. **What happens in the poem?** The poem advises that a person who rises early and bathes often will remain healthy and attractive.
3. **Who are the characters in the poem?** The characters are the narrator and the maid.
4. **Does the poem teach us anything?** The poem suggests we rise early and bathe often.
5. **Describe the poem picture.** The poem picture shows a maid at sunrise, gathering dew from the bushes to wash.

LESSON 54

1. **What is the title of the poem?** The poem title is "Sulky Sue."
2. **What happens in the poem?** A girl faces the corner for being sulky.
3. **Who are the characters in the poem?** The characters are the narrator and Sulky Sue.
4. **Does the poem teach us anything?** The poem reminds us that there may be consequences for having a bad attitude.
5. **Describe the poem picture.** The poem picture shows a little girl placing her sulky doll in the corner.

LESSON 55

1. **What is the title of the poem?** The poem title is "Bobby Snooks."
2. **What happens in the poem?** Bobby Snooks studies and is loved by his teacher. Jack Spry gets into trouble and ends up with a black eye and a broken nose.
3. **Who are the characters in the poem?** The characters are the narrator, Bobby Snooks, his usher, his master, and Jack Spry.
4. **Does the poem teach us anything?** The poem reminds us that working hard tends to lead to admiration and happiness. Troublemaking tends to lead to sadness and problems.
5. **Describe the poem picture.** The poem picture shows Jack Spry with his black eye and broken nose, dragging his books behind him and looking sad.

LESSON 56
1. **What is the title of the poem?** The poem title is "The Man in the Moon."
2. **What happens in the poem?** The Man in the Moon falls, starts for Norwich, and burns his mouth on cold porridge.
3. **Who are the characters in the poem?** The characters are the narrator and the Man in the Moon.
4. **Describe the poem picture.** The picture shows the Man in the Moon holding his burned mouth. A cauldron of porridge is overturned nearby.
5. **Why did the Man in the Moon burn his mouth on cold porridge?** The Man in the Moon is from the moon and must be different than humans from Earth.

LESSON 57
1. **What is the title of the poem?** The poem title is "Poor Old Robinson Crusoe."
2. **What happens in the poem?** In the poem, a poor man wears a coat made from a goat.
3. **Who are the characters in the poem?** The characters are the narrator and Robinson Crusoe.
4. **Describe the poem picture.** The poem picture shows a poor man carrying a gun and an umbrella on a beach. A dog walks by his side.

LESSON 58
1. **What is the title of the poem?** The poem title is "Cock-crow."
2. **What happens in the poem?** The poem gives advice for successful living.
3. **What is the setting of the poem?** The poem takes place at a farm or rural location.
4. **Who are the characters in the poem?** The characters are the rooster and the narrator.
5. **Does the poem teach us anything?** The poem tells us to go to bed and rise early to be healthy, smart, and successful.
6. **Describe the poem picture.** The picture shows a boy rising early in the morning.

LESSON 59
1. **What is the title of the poem?** The poem title is "Tommy Snooks."
2. **What happens in the poem?** Tommy asks Bessy if she will marry him the very next day.
3. **What is the setting of the poem?** The poem takes place outside on a walk.
4. **Who are the characters in the poem?** The characters are the narrator, Tommy Snooks, and Bessy Brooks.
5. **Describe the poem picture.** The poem picture shows Tommy and Bessy walking. A church is visible on the horizon.

LESSON 60
1. **What is the title of the poem?** The poem title is "The Blacksmith."
2. **What happens in the poem?** The narrator asks a blacksmith to shoe his horse. The blacksmith agrees and performs the job.
3. **What is the setting of the poem?** The poem takes place at the Blacksmith's shop.
4. **Who are the characters in the poem?** The characters are the blacksmith and the narrator.
5. **Describe the poem picture.** The poem picture shows a boy taking his toy horse to a blacksmith.

LESSON 61
1. **What is the title of the poem?** The poem title is "Cock-A-Doodle-Doo."
2. **What happens in the poem?** The fiddler loses his stick and can't play. The lady loses her shoe and cannot dance. The narrator nonsensically claims the lady will dance without her shoe until the fiddler finds his stick.
3. **Who are the characters in the poem?** The characters are the master, the dame, and the rooster narrator.
4. **Describe the poem picture.** The picture shows a fiddler without a stick and a lady without a shoe. A rooster stands between them.

LESSON 62
1. **What is the title of the poem?** The poem title is "Dapple-Gray."
2. **What happens in the poem?** A boy lends his pony to a lady. The lady mistreats the pony. The boy vows never to lend his pony again.
3. **Who are the characters in the poem?** The characters are the narrator, the boy, the lady, and the pony.
4. **Does the poem teach us anything?** The poem teaches us to be careful about who we trust.
5. **Describe the poem picture.** The picture shows the lady, the boy, and the pony standing together. The lady clutches a long whip.

LESSON 63
1. **What is the title of the poem?** The poem title is "Coffee and Tea."
2. **What happens in the poem?** Two sisters fight and fall out because one likes tea and the other likes coffee.
3. **Who are the characters in the poem?** The characters are the narrator and her sister, Molly.
4. **Does the poem teach us anything?** The poem teaches us that many disagreements are over petty things.
5. **Describe the poem picture.** The picture shows two girls holding cups. One turns her back and looks angry. The other raises her finger.

LESSON 64
1. **What is the title of the poem?** The poem title is "The Little Girl with a Curl."
2. **What happens in the poem?** The narrator describes a little girl, who acts in extremes. She is either very good or horrid.
3. **Who are the characters in the poem?** The characters are the narrator and the little girl.
4. **Does the poem teach us anything?** To poem suggests that even if we are very good some of the time, it does not make up for being horrid other times.
5. **Describe the poem picture.** The poem picture shows the little girl sitting in a chair and looking grumpy.

LESSON 65
1. **What is the title of the poem?** The poem title is "Candle-Saving."
2. **What happens in the poem?** Honest John advises that the only way to save candles is to put them out.
3. **Who are the characters in the poem?** The characters are honest John and the narrator.
4. **Does the poem teach us anything?** The poem teaches us there is no trick to preserving candles beyond putting them out and using them sparingly.
5. **Describe the poem picture.** The poem picture shows a man lifting one finger and holding a candle.

LESSON 66
1. **What is the title of the poem?** The poem title is "Ladybird."
2. **What happens in the poem?** The narrator tries to convince a ladybug to fly away.
3. **What is the setting of the poem?** The poem takes place outdoors.
4. **Who are the characters in the poem?** The characters are the narrator and the ladybug.
5. **Describe the poem picture.** The poem picture shows a boy with a ladybug on his hand. A girl stands next to him and watches.

LESSON 67
1. **What is the title of the poem?** The poem title is "Caesar's Song."
2. **Why do you think the title is "Caesar's Song?"** Caesar may be the dog's name, and his song is his bark.
3. **What happens in the poem?** A dog says he belongs to Tom Tinker.
4. **Who are the characters in the poem?** The characters are the narrator, the dog, and Tom Tinker.
5. **Describe the poem picture.** The poem picture shows a boy looking over a stone fence at a dog tied to a dog house.

LESSON 68
1. **What is the title of the poem?** The poem title is "As I was Going Along."
2. **What happens in the poem?** The narrator sings and walks a long time.
3. **What is the setting of the poem?** The poem takes place on a long road.
4. **Who are the characters in the poem?** The character is the singing, walking narrator.
5. **Describe the poem picture.** The poem picture shows a boy strolling down a path with his hands in his pockets.

LESSON 69
1. **What is the title of the poem?** The poem title is "Little Jack Horner."
2. **What happens in the poem?** Jack puts his thumb in a pie, pulls out a plumb, and says he is a good boy.
3. **What is the setting of the poem?** The poem takes place in a house.
4. **Who are the characters in the poem?** The characters are the narrator and Jack Horner.
5. **Describe the poem picture.** Jack sits in the corner with his Christmas pie. A kitty looks on.

LESSON 70
1. **What is the title of the poem?** The poem title is "Mary, Mary, Quite Contrary."
2. **What happens in the poem?** The narrator asks Mary about her garden. Mary describes her garden.
3. **Who are the characters in the poem?** The characters are the narrator, Mary, and Mary's pretty maids.
4. **Describe the poem picture.** The picture shows Mary looking at her garden. There are silver bells in the trees, cockle shells lining the path, and pretty maids lined up beyond the brick wall.

LESSON 71
1. **What is the title of the poem?** The poem title is "Mary's Canary."
2. **What happens in the poem?** Mary has a pretty bird. She enjoys listening to the bird sing.
3. **Who are the characters in the poem?** The characters are the narrator, Mary, and her bird.
4. **Describe the poem picture.** The picture shows Mary sitting on a bench next to her caged canary.

LESSON 72
1. **What is the title of the poem?** The poem title is "The Little Bird."
2. **What happens in the poem?** The narrator sees a little bird and asks it to stay, but it flies away.
3. **What is the setting of the poem?** The poem takes place in a room with a window.
4. **Who are the characters in the poem?** The characters are the narrator and a bird.
5. **Describe the poem picture.** The poem picture shows a boy looking out an open window.

REFERENCES AND ADDITIONAL READING

1. *Cover Image*
   a. Holeysocksart. "Puddle Fun" (CC0 Creative Commons, {PD-US})
   b. Source: *pixabay.com/en/boots-splash-rain-puddle-fun-774533/*
   c. License: This work is in the public domain in the United States because it was published under a CC0 Creative Commons license, releasing this work into the public domain worldwide.
2. *Poem Text and Illustrations*
   a. Illustrated by Wright, Blanche Fisher. "The Real Mother Goose" (1916, {PD-US})
   b. License: This work is in the public domain in the United States because it was published (or registered with the U.S. Copyright Office) before January 1, 1923.

ABOUT THE AUTHOR

Sonja Glumich is a scientist, educator, wife, and mother who is inspired by Charlotte Mason's living works approach to homeschooling. She is the founder of Under the Home (underthehome.org), an online homeschool curriculum featuring low-cost courses in art history, poetry, prose, music, history, science, studio art, mathematics, reading, and Shakespeare. Sonja and her husband, Chris, homeschool their three school-aged children using the Under the Home curriculum as featured in this book.

Sonja graduated magna cum laude with bachelor's degrees in biology, chemistry, and computer science and later earned a master's degree in information technology. She has also completed education classes and student teaching leading to certification to teach secondary science.

Sonja has experience teaching students of all ages, from preschool to graduate school, including as a middle school and high school science public school teacher. She has also served as an Adjunct Professor for Syracuse University and co-created two graduate-level cyber courses. She currently works as a computer scientist for the Air Force Research Laboratory. Her current research and education interests are security systems engineering, cyber vulnerability assessments, and everything homeschooling.

Made in the USA
Monee, IL
12 March 2025

13886804R00131